TALES OF WONDER

Volume 2

TALES OF WONDER

8 ESSENTIAL FAIRY TALES + DISCUSSION QUESTIONS

Ed. by Brian Phillips, Matthew Bianco, and David Kern

CiRCE Institute Publishing
Concord, NC

Published in the USA
by the CiRCE Institute
Second printing
© CiRCE Institute 2019

ISBN: 978-0-9991466-6-8

The text for each story found in this collection is taken from the public domain.

For information:
CiRCE Institute
81 McCachern Blvd.
Concord, NC 28025
www.circeinstitute.org

Cover design by Graeme Pitman.

Printed in the United States of America.

TABLE OF CONTENTS

THE TALES

How to Use This Book

··

The book you now hold contains some of the world's greatest fairy tales, from the marvelous collections of Andrew Lang, Hans Christian Andersen, and Charles Perrault. And while some of these stories originated once-upon-a-time, in lands far, far away, they remain as magical and powerful as ever.

Each chapter in this book contains the text of the story, followed by three sets of questions related to that fairy tale.

- *The first set of questions can be asked "while reading" the story aloud to your children, students, or group.*
- *The second set of questions work well "after reading" the story.*
- *Finally, each chapter ends with a "Listening for Echoes" exercise, which gives you, your class, or group the opportunity to explore connections between the fairy tale you read and other stories.*

The goal of these questions is not to get one particular answer, but to learn to read and discuss stories skillfully.

WHY TALES OF WONDER?

In *An Experiment in Criticism*, C.S. Lewis asks, "What then is the good of—what is even the defense for—occupying our hearts with stories of what never happened and entering vicariously into feelings which we should try to avoid having in our own person? Or of fixing our inner eye earnestly on things that can never exist?"[1] In self-reply, he offers, "The nearest I have yet got to an answer is that we seek an enlargement of our being. We want to be more than ourselves. . . . We want to see with other eyes, to imagine with other imaginations, to feel with other hearts, as well as with our own . . . We demand windows . . . In reading great literature I become a thousand men and yet remain myself."[2] When we enter great stories, we are changed. We become different people.

Children seem to understand this far better than "grown-ups." They aren't satisfied simply with hearing stories, but they feel the need to act them out, to memorize them, and even to dress as the characters.

---

1. Quoted in "The Christian Imagination," (Colorado Springs: Shaw Books, 2002), 51-52.

2. Ibid.

Bit by bit, as we age, we leave behind such visible displays of how story changes us. The reenactments fade; the games become mere recollection. Yet, as Anthony Esolen argues in *Ten Ways to Destroy the Imagination of Your Child*, they are those "memories of play that no one regrets, and that are almost the only things an old man can look back on with complete satisfaction."[3]

Esolen's words reveal that the modern abandonment of fairy tales and classic stories is far more tragic than we seem to realize, devastating childhood and, in turn, adulthood as well. We deny grown men the "memories of play that no one regrets" by denying them the stories that make for play in childhood.

But far more is at stake than pleasant memories. When children are denied access to noble stories and fairy tales—whether through omission, or through the more common and deadlier method of "moralizing"—their moral growth is stunted. They are removed from some of the greatest models of honor, wisdom, courage, selflessness, and other significant virtues. Yet, as C.S. Lewis lamented, we pretend to be shocked when such virtues are absent in the lives of those children:

> *And all the time—such is the tragi-comedy of our situation—we continue to clamor for those very qualities we are rendering impossible. You can hardly open a periodical without coming across the statement that what our civilization needs is more "drive," or dynamism, or self-sacrifice, or "creativity." In a sort of ghastly simplicity we remove the organ and demand the function. We make men without chests and expect of them virtue and enterprise. We laugh at honor and are shocked to find traitors in our midst. We castrate and bid the geldings be fruitful.[4]*

If possible, the situation is made more tragic by the obvious presence of a child's "moral constitution." As Vigen Guroian observed in the

---

3. Anthony Esolen, *Ten Ways to Destroy the Imagination of Your Child* (Wilmington: ISI Books, 2010), xii.

4. Lewis, *Abolition of Man* (San Francisco: Harper, 2001), 26.

opening words of *Tending the Heart of Virtue*:

> *Children are vitally concerned with distinguishing good from evil and*
> *truth from falsehood . . . . Every parent who has read a fairy tale to a*
> *young son or daughter is familiar with . . . a universal refrain of child-*
> *hood. "But is he a good person or a bad one?" What greater proof or*
> *assurance could we want that God and nature have endowed human*
> *beings with a moral constitution that needs to be nurtured and culti-*
> *vated?[5]*

Fairy tales and classic stories are some of the greatest tools for nur-
turing and cultivating the moral constitution, or moral imagination.

But aren't there more direct routes? Is it not much more efficient to
simply tell children what they should and should not do, rather than
relying on stories? Guroian addresses this, saying, "Mere instruction in
morality is not sufficient to nurture the virtues. It might even backfire,
especially when the presentation is heavily exhortative and the pupil's
will is coerced."[6] We must, to borrow from Flannery O'Connor, "show"
virtue and goodness to our children, not simply "tell" them about it.

The removal of classic stories poses only the most obvious threat to
a child's moral imagination, not the most dangerous. While celebrat-
ing that the "Grendel" of omission has been vanquished, many parents who do read good stories to their children fail to notice Grendel's
mother, moralization, lurking. She is, indeed, a far deadlier enemy.
When we moralize, we reduce ethics and morality to a set of propositions, as if knowledge of those propositions somehow guarantees true
internalization of them.

Again, Guroian writes:

> *The deep truths of a good story, especially fairy tales, cannot be re-*
> *vealed through discursive analysis—otherwise, why tell the story?*

---

5. Vigen Guroian, *Tending the Heart of Virtue* (New York: Oxford University Press, 1998), 3–4.

6. Ibid., 20.

Rather, these truths must be experienced through the story itself and savored in the immediacy of the moment that unfolds with the impending danger of the quest or the joy of reunion with the beloved.[7]

Education will always be moral, but it need not collapse under the error of moralism, which despite even the purest intentions, produces no lasting virtue. Ethical platitudes show themselves anemic in the face of truth, goodness, and beauty demonstrated in great stories. *Tales of Wonder* is our small introduction to some of those stories. We hope you enjoy it as much as we enjoyed making it!

Brian Phillips
Season after Pentecost, 2018

---

7. Ibid., 15-16.

THE POWER OF STORY: TOWARD THE TRANSFORMATION OF SOULS

I n her essay "The Necessity of the Classics," Louise Cowan tells the story of *Kagemusha*, a film by legendary Japanese director Akira Kurosawa. Simply put, it is the story of a beggar who is about to be put to death for stealing, but his execution is stayed because the soldiers notice that he bears a remarkably close resemblance to their chief. He becomes the chief's understudy—learning his mannerisms, voice, walk, and personality. And he gradually takes on both the leader's internal and external "dignity." By the time the chief dies, the beggar has become so skilled as an understudy that he is able to keep up the ruse for months.

Eventually, of course, the ruler's death is discovered, and the understudy becomes the beggar once again. Yet, Cowan notes:

A strange thing has happened: This pretender has developed a genuine sense of responsibility that cannot so lightly be dismissed. The burden of leadership, with its peculiar blend of selflessness and pride, has become his own. Despite his low station, he follows along after the troops in battle and stands at the last defending

the banner of his defeated people, exposing himself to the enemy's
onslaughts when all others have fallen. . . . Is this heroic gesture
still part of the act? Where does it come from, this apparent great-
ness of soul that finally requires in a counterfeit role an authentic
death? . . . through schooling in a tradition. Such magnanimity,
we are shown, requires mimesis—imitation. To remake oneself in
the image of something that calls to greatness demands a heroic
tradition displaying heroic models.

Truly great literature has a similar effect. It gives us models of virtue, wisdom, and goodness to imitate, as well as pictures of evil to avoid. It calls us to true nobility of soul. As C.S. Lewis wrote, "those of us who have been true readers all our life seldom fully realize the enormous extension of our being which we owe to authors."

This is why the book you're holding right now exists.

As Christians, we are blessed to be able to read classic literature with a more complete picture of the truth, goodness, and beauty demonstrated therein, while at the same time seeing God's common grace at work—even in the stories and lives of pagans. Through the stories of Achilles, Odysseus, Aeneas, Beowulf, Dante, Hamlet, and others we can learn both good and bad lessons that drive us to wisdom and virtue in Christ.

Scripture offers stories of saints and sinners gone before, stories of great triumph (Heb. 11) and great fall (1 Cor. 10:1-13). Similarly, classic literature enlightens through the struggles, victories, and failures of complicated characters. As Leland Ryken wrote, "Literature is built on a grand paradox: It is a make-believe world that nonetheless reminds us of real life and clarifies it for us."[1] Or as G.K. Chesterton put it in *Orthodoxy*, there are no stories so "sensible" and revealing as fairy tales.

Indeed, as Chesterton further explores in *Orthodoxy*, fairy tales (and poetry and great works of fiction) provide an antidote to the insipid vacuousness of contemporary thought. The fairy tale, he argues, "dis-

---

1. Leland Ryken, *The Christian Imagination* (Colorado Springs: Shaw Books, 2002), 25.

cusses what a sane man will do in a mad world."[2] And it does this not by offering step-by-step instructions for being successful or by changing worldviews or even by debunking the logic behind modern modes of life. Rather, fairy tales offer a more complex view of life because they offer young people (really all people) a way of interacting with the mystical realities at work in the universe, the deep poetry at the heart of human existence. Another way of saying this is that they transform us by opening us up to what Chesterton called "an infinite sea," giving us the capacity for "exaltation and expansion," a "world to stretch" ourselves in. Fairy tales allow us to "get our head into the heavens" even as it's impossible—and foolish to attempt—to stuff the "heavens into our heads."

So the power and beauty of the fairy tale is that it takes us beyond morals and lessons and actually transforms our souls. And, ultimately, this is our goal, is it not? It's well and good to tell our children and/ or students that something is true, good, and beautiful. Sometimes it's even necessary. But how much more powerful is it to offer them something that can make them new—something that can open their eyes to the transcendent. Something that shows itself to be true, good, and beautiful. Something that reveals the truth, goodness, and beauty at the heart of the universe not by lists and equations and logic, but simply by existing.

Teachers and parents sometimes talk about giving our children something "they can grab on to." But one of the grand paradoxes of the fairy tale is that it can transform our children without the need for grasping. Because they are inherently poetic, fairy tales reveal truth by their very nature. All one has to do is experience them, to pretend to be a part of them.

This book is an attempt to make such experience possible. We hope that it can be a small wave on the infinite sea Chesterton spoke of, that it can be a door into a world where our students can "stretch" towards the heavens, a bit at a time, until their heads poke through the clouds

---

2. G.K. Chesteron, *The Collected Works of G.K. Chesterton* (San Francisco: Ignatius, 1986), 218.

and their eyes take in the sort of poetry to which wonder is the only appropriate response. If we can teach them to revel in that wonder, to be comfortable (and take joy) in it, then truly their souls will grow capable of great nobility, and they will be able to slay the dragons in their paths, resist the witches who tempt them, and persist even in the darkest of woods. With their heads in the clouds, their feet will triumph on the ground.

We pray this is your experience.

The Editors
Lent, 2019

About the Storytellers

Hans Christian Andersen (1805-1875) was a Danish author who penned novels, poems, and plays, but is almost exclusively remembered for his fairy tales. His more than three thousand fairy tales have been translated into over one hundred languages and continue to be published in multiple editions around the world. Among his most beloved tales are "Thumbelina," "The Princess and the Pea," "The Emperor's New Suit," and "The Ugly Duckling" (which are included in this book). Andersen endured a difficult childhood that included the death of his father and tumultuous years in school. At one point, Andersen said, some of his teachers openly discouraged his ambitions to become a writer. Fortunately for us, he did not listen.

Andrew Lang (1844-1912) was an accomplished scholar in multiple areas, earning entrance into the Fellowship of the British Academy in 1906. Though his academic fields included history, anthropology, and multiple written volumes on the epics of Homer, Lang is best remembered for his collections of fairy tales, arranged in twelve multi-colored volumes, published from 1889-1910. Born and educated in Scotland, Lang eventually attended Oxford University and was named a fellow at Oxford's Merton College. His wife Leonora, whom he married in 1875, assisted him in collecting and translating a number of the fairy tales in his set.

Charles Perrault (1628-1703) was born to a wealthy Parisian family, received an excellent education, and even worked as an advisor to King Louis XIV. Perrault's adult life, however, would have its challenges. In 1678, his young wife, Marie, died and Perrault was dismissed from his job as government secretary in 1695. At that point, he devoted himself to his children and to writing and collecting fairy tales. Perrault published *Tales of Mother Goose* in 1697, and his renderings of "Puss in Boots," "Cinderella," and "Sleeping Beauty" (which is included in this book) remain some of the most familiar.

THE TALES

GUSTAVE DORE, 1862

SLEEPING BEAUTY

By Charles Perrault

◆ ◆ ◆

Although earlier versions of the tale are believed to date back as early as the 1300s, "Sleeping Beauty"—also entitled "The Sleeping Beauty in the Woods" and "Little Briar Rose"—was first published by Charles Perrault in 1697. This version, presented here, could be divided into two main sections. The first ends with the marriage of Sleeping Beauty and the Prince. The second part picks up after their wedding with a shocking revelation about the Prince's mother and continues to the end. Readers will find it rewarding to compare those two sections, not only with one another, but also with the overall narrative of Scripture and the great Christian creeds (The Apostles' Creed and the Nicene Creed).

The Tale

....

Once upon a time there lived a king and queen who were grieved, more grieved than words can tell, because they had no children. They tried the waters of every country, made vows and pilgrimages, and did everything that could be done, but without result. At last, however, the queen found that her wishes were fulfilled, and in due course she gave birth to a daughter.

A grand christening was held, and all the fairies that could be found in the realm (they numbered seven in all) were invited to be godmothers to the little princess. This was done so that by means of the gifts which each in turn would bestow upon her (in accordance with the fairy custom of those days) the princess might be endowed with every imaginable perfection.

When the christening ceremony was over, all the company returned to the king's palace, where a great banquet was held in honor of the fairies. Places were laid for them in magnificent style, and before each was placed a solid gold casket containing a spoon, fork, and knife of fine gold, set with diamonds and rubies. But just as all were sitting down to table an aged fairy was seen to enter, whom no one had thought to invite—the reason being that for more than fifty years she had never quitted the tower in which she lived, and people had supposed her to be dead or bewitched.

By the king's orders a place was laid for her, but it was impossible to give her a golden casket like the others, for only seven had been made

for the seven fairies. The old creature believed that she was intention-
ally slighted, and muttered threats between her teeth.

She was overheard by one of the young fairies, who was seated nearby. The latter, guessing that some mischievous gift might be bestowed
upon the little princess, hid behind the tapestry as soon as the company left the table. Her intention was to be the last to speak, and so to
have the power of counteracting, as far as possible, any evil which the
old fairy might do.

Presently the fairies began to bestow their gifts upon the princess.
The youngest ordained that she should be the most beautiful person
in the world; the next, that she should have the temper of an angel; the
third, that she should do everything with wonderful grace; the fourth,
that she should dance to perfection; the fifth, that she should sing like
a nightingale; and the sixth, that she should play every kind of music
with the utmost skill.

It was now the turn of the aged fairy. Shaking her head, in token
of spite rather than of infirmity, she declared that the princess should
prick her hand with a spindle, and die of it. A shudder ran through the
company at this terrible gift. All eyes were filled with tears.

But at this moment the young fairy stepped forth from behind the
tapestry.

"Take comfort, your Majesties," she cried in a loud voice. "Your
daughter shall not die. My power, it is true, is not enough to undo all
that my aged kinswoman has decreed. The princess will indeed prick
her hand with a spindle. But instead of dying she shall merely fall into
a profound slumber that will last a hundred years. At the end of that
time a king's son shall come to awaken her."

The king, in an attempt to avert the unhappy doom pronounced by
the old fairy, at once published an edict forbidding all persons, under
pain of death, to use a spinning wheel or keep a spindle in the house.

At the end of fifteen or sixteen years the king and queen happened
one day to be away, on pleasure bent. The princess was running about
the castle, and going upstairs from room to room she came at length
to a garret at the top of a tower, where an old serving woman sat alone

with her distaff, spinning. This good woman had never heard speak of the king's proclamation forbidding the use of spinning wheels.

"What are you doing, my good woman?" asked the princess.

"I am spinning, my pretty child," replied the dame, not knowing who she was.

"Oh, what fun!" rejoined the princess. "How do you do it? Let me try and see if I can do it equally well."

DISCUSS AS YOU READ:
SHOULD THE PRINCESS TRY USING THE SPINNING WHEEL? WHY OR WHY NOT?

Partly because she was too hasty, partly because she was a little heedless, but also because the fairy decree had ordained it, no sooner had she seized the spindle than she pricked her hand and fell down in a swoon.

In great alarm the good dame cried out for help. People came running from every quarter to the princess. They threw water on her face, chafed her with their hands, and rubbed her temples with the royal essence of Hungary. But nothing would restore her.

Then the king, who had been brought upstairs by the commotion, remembered the fairy prophecy. Feeling certain that what had happened was inevitable, since the fairies had decreed it, he gave orders that the princess should be placed in the finest apartment in the palace, upon a bed embroidered in gold and silver.

You would have thought her an angel, so fair was she to behold. The trance had not taken away the lovely color of her complexion. Her cheeks were delicately flushed, her lips like coral. Her eyes, indeed, were closed, but her gentle breathing could be heard, and it was therefore plain that she was not dead. The king commanded that she should be left to sleep in peace until the hour of her awakening should come.

When the accident happened to the princess, the good fairy who had saved her life by condemning her to sleep a hundred years was in the kingdom of Mataquin, twelve thousand leagues away. She was instantly warned of it, however, by a little dwarf who had a pair of seven-league boots, which are boots that enable one to cover seven leagues at a single step. The fairy set off at once, and within an hour her chariot of fire, drawn by dragons, was seen approaching.

The king handed her down from her chariot, and she approved of all that he had done. But being gifted with great powers of foresight, she bethought herself that when the princess came to be awakened, she would be much distressed to find herself all alone in the old castle. And this is what she did.

She touched with her wand everybody (except the king and queen) who was in the castle—governesses, maids of honor, ladies-in-waiting, gentlemen, officers, stewards, cooks, scullions, errand boys, guards, porters, pages, footmen. She touched likewise all the horses in the stables, with their grooms, the big mastiffs in the courtyard, and little Puff, the pet dog of the princess, who was lying on the bed beside his mistress. The moment she had touched them they all fell asleep, to awaken only at the same moment as their mistress. Thus they would always be ready with their service whenever she should require it. The very spits before the fire, loaded with partridges and pheasants, subsided into slumber, and the fire as well. All was done in a moment, for the fairies do not take long over their work.

Then the king and queen kissed their dear child, without waking her, and left the castle.

Proclamations were issued, forbidding any approach to it, but these warnings were not needed, for within a quarter of an hour there grew up all round the park so vast a quantity of trees big and small, with interlacing brambles and thorns, that neither man nor beast could penetrate them. The tops alone of the castle towers could be seen, and these only from a distance. Thus did the fairy's magic contrive that the princess, during all the time of her slumber, should have naught whatever to fear from prying eyes.

At the end of a hundred years the throne had passed to another fam-

---

DISCUSS AS YOU READ:
DO THE BRAMBLES AND THORNS REMIND YOU OF ANY OTHER STORIES? EXPLAIN.

---

ily from that of the sleeping princess. One day the king's son chanced to go a-hunting that way, and seeing in the distance some towers in the midst of a large and dense forest, he asked what they were. His attendants told him in reply the various stories which they had heard. Some said there was an old castle haunted by ghosts, others that all the witches of the neighborhood held their revels there. The favorite tale was that in the castle lived an ogre, who carried thither all the children whom he could catch. There he devoured them at his leisure, and since he was the only person who could force a passage through the wood nobody had been able to pursue him.

While the prince was wondering what to believe, an old peasant took up the tale.

"Your Highness," said he, "more than fifty years ago I heard my father say that in this castle lies a princess, the most beautiful that has ever been seen. It is her doom to sleep there for a hundred years, and then to be awakened by a king's son, for whose coming she waits."

This story fired the young prince. He jumped immediately to the conclusion that it was for him to see so gay an adventure through, and impelled alike by the wish for love and glory, he resolved to set about it on the spot.

Hardly had he taken a step towards the wood when the tall trees, the brambles and the thorns, separated of themselves and made a path for him. He turned in the direction of the castle, and espied it at the end of a long avenue. This avenue he entered, and was surprised to notice that the trees closed up again as soon as he had passed, so that none of his retinue were able to follow him. A young and gallant prince is always brave, however; so he continued on his way, and presently reached a large forecourt.

The sight that now met his gaze was enough to fill him with an icy fear. The silence of the place was dreadful, and death seemed all about him. The recumbent figures of men and animals had all the appearance of being lifeless, until he perceived by the pimply noses and ruddy faces of the porters, that they merely slept. It was plain, too, from their glasses, in which were still some dregs of wine, that they had fallen asleep while drinking.

The prince made his way into a great courtyard, paved with marble, and mounting the staircase entered the guardroom. Here the guards were lined up on either side in two ranks, their muskets on their shoulders, snoring their hardest. Through several apartments crowded with ladies and gentlemen in waiting, some seated, some standing, but all asleep, he pushed on, and so came at last to a chamber which was decked all over with gold. There he encountered the most beautiful sight he had ever seen. Reclining upon a bed, the curtains of which on every side were drawn back, was a princess of seemingly some fifteen or sixteen summers, whose radiant beauty had an almost unearthly luster.

Trembling in his admiration he drew near and went on his knees beside her. At the same moment, the hour of disenchantment having come, the princess awoke, and bestowed upon him a look more tender than a first glance might seem to warrant.

"Is it you, dear prince?" she said. "You have been long in coming!"

Charmed by these words, and especially by the manner in which they were said, the prince scarcely knew how to express his delight and gratification. He declared that he loved her better than he loved himself. His words were faltering, but they pleased the more for that. The less there is of eloquence, the more there is of love.

Her embarrassment was less than his, and that is not to be wondered at, since she had had time to think of what she would say to him. It seems (although the story says nothing about it) that the good fairy had beguiled her long slumber with pleasant dreams. To be brief, after four hours of talking they had not succeeded in uttering one half of the things they had to say to each other.

Now the whole palace had awakened with the princess. Everyone went about his business, and since they were not all in love they presently began to feel mortally hungry. The lady-in-waiting, who was suffering like the rest, at length lost patience, and in a loud voice called out to the princess that supper was served.

The princess was already fully dressed, and in most magnificent style. As he helped her to rise, the prince refrained from telling her that her clothes, with the straight collar which she wore, were like those to which his grandmother had been accustomed. And in truth, they in no way detracted from her beauty.

They passed into an apartment hung with mirrors, and were there served with supper by the stewards of the household, while the fiddles and oboes played some old music and played it remarkably well, considering they had not played at all for just upon a hundred years. A little later, when supper was over, the chaplain married them in the castle chapel, and in due course, attended by the courtiers in waiting, they retired to rest.

They slept but little, however. The princess, indeed, had not much need of sleep, and as soon as morning came the prince took his leave of her. He returned to the city, and told his father, who was awaiting him with some anxiety, that he had lost himself while hunting in the forest, but had obtained some black bread and cheese from a charcoal burner, in whose hovel he had passed the night.

His royal father, being of an easygoing nature, believed the tale, but his mother was not so easily hoodwinked. She noticed that he now went hunting every day, and that he always had an excuse handy when he had slept two or three nights from home. She felt certain, therefore, that he had some love affair.

Two whole years passed since the marriage of the prince and princess, and during that time they had two children. The first, a daughter, was called "Dawn," while the second, a boy, was named "Day," because he seemed even more beautiful than his sister.

Many a time the queen told her son that he ought to settle down in life. She tried in this way to make him confide in her, but he did not dare to trust her with his secret. Despite the affection which he bore her, he was afraid of his mother, for she came of a race of ogres, and the king had only married her for her wealth.

It was whispered at the court that she had ogrish instincts, and that when little children were near her she had the greatest difficulty in the world to keep herself from pouncing on them. No wonder the prince was reluctant to say a word.

But at the end of two years the king died, and the prince found himself on the throne. He then made public announcement of his marriage, and went in state to fetch his royal consort from her castle. With her two children beside her she made a triumphal entry into the capital of her husband's realm.

Some time afterwards the king declared war on his neighbor, the Emperor Cantalabutte. He appointed the queen mother as regent in his absence, and entrusted his wife and children to her care.

He expected to be away at the war for the whole of the summer, and as soon as he was gone the queen mother sent her daughter-in-law and the two children to a country mansion in the forest. This she did that she might be able the more easily to gratify her horrible longings. A few days later she went there and in the evening summoned the chief steward.

"For my dinner tomorrow," she told him, "I will eat little Dawn."

"Oh, Madam!" exclaimed the steward.

"That is my will," said the queen; and she spoke in the tones of an ogre who longs for raw meat. "You will serve her with piquant sauce," she added.

DISCUSS AS YOU READ:
WHAT SHOULD THE CHIEF SERVANT DO?

The poor man, seeing plainly that it was useless to trifle with an ogress, took his big knife and went up to little Dawn's chamber. She was at that time four years old, and when she came running with a smile to greet him, flinging her arms round his neck and coaxing him to give her some sweets, he burst into tears, and let the knife fall from his hand.

Presently he went down to the yard behind the house, and slaughtered a young lamb. For this he made so delicious a sauce that his mistress declared she had never eaten anything so good.

At the same time the steward carried little Dawn to his wife, and bade the latter hide her in the quarters which they had below the yard.

Eight days later the wicked queen summoned her steward again.

"For my supper," she announced, "I will eat little Day."

The steward made no answer, being determined to trick her as he had done previously. He went in search of little Day, whom he found with a tiny foil in his hand, making brave passes—though he was but three years old—at a big monkey. He carried him off to his wife, who stowed him away in hiding with little Dawn. To the ogress the steward served up, in place of Day, a young kid so tender that she found it surpassingly delicious.

So far, so good. But there came an evening when this evil queen again addressed the steward.

"I have a mind," she said, "to eat the queen with the same sauce as you served with her children."

This time the poor steward despaired of being able to practice another deception. The young queen was twenty years old, without counting the hundred years she had been asleep. Her skin, though white and beautiful, had become a little tough, and what animal could he possibly find that would correspond to her? He made up his mind that if he would save his own life he must kill the queen, and went upstairs to her apartment determined to do the deed once and for all. Goading himself into a rage he drew his knife and entered the young queen's chamber, but a reluctance to give her no moment of grace made him repeat respectfully the command which he had received from the queen mother.

"Do it! Do it!" she cried, baring her neck to him. "Carry out the order you have been given! Then once more I shall see my children, my poor children that I loved so much!"

Nothing had been said to her when the children were stolen away, and she believed them to be dead.

The poor steward was overcome by compassion. "No, no, Madam," he declared. "You shall not die, but you shall certainly see your children again. That will be in my quarters, where I have hidden them. I shall make the queen eat a young hind in place of you, and thus trick her once more."

Without more ado he led her to his quarters, and leaving her there to embrace and weep over her children, proceeded to cook a hind with such art that the queen mother ate it for her supper with as much appetite as if it had indeed been the young queen.

The queen mother felt well satisfied with her cruel deeds, and planned to tell the king, on his return, that savage wolves had devoured his consort and his children. It was her habit, however, to prowl often about the courts and alleys of the mansion, in the hope of scenting raw meat, and one evening she heard the little boy Day crying in a basement cellar. The child was weeping because his mother had threatened to whip him for some naughtiness, and she heard at the same time the voice of Dawn begging forgiveness for her brother.

The ogress recognized the voices of the queen and her children, and was enraged to find she had been tricked. The next morning, in tones so affrighting that all trembled, she ordered a huge vat to be brought into the middle of the courtyard. This she filled with vipers and toads, with snakes and serpents of every kind, intending to cast into it the queen and her children, and the steward with his wife and serving girl. By her command these were brought forward, with their hands tied behind their backs.

There they were, and her minions were making ready to cast them into the vat, when into the courtyard rode the king! Nobody had expected him so soon, but he had traveled posthaste. Filled with amazement, he demanded to know what this horrible spectacle meant.

None dared tell him, and at that moment the ogress, enraged at what confronted her, threw herself head foremost into the vat, and was devoured on the instant by the hideous creatures she had placed in it.

The king could not but be sorry, for after all she was his mother; but it was not long before he found ample consolation in his beautiful wife and children.

THE DISCUSSION

First, briefly narrate the story back.

Questions to ask after reading the story:
• How does the ending make you feel? Why does the ending make you feel that way?
• Compare the aged fairy and the queen mother. How are they alike? How are they different?
• Sleeping Beauty and the Prince had two children. What were their names? Why might those names be important in the story?
• What gifts were given to Sleeping Beauty by the first six fairies? What do they all have in common?
• With those gifts in mind (see question above), why was the curse of the aged fairy particularly terrible?
• Do the characters remind you of characters from any other story? Explain.

Listening for Echoes
"Sleeping Beauty" invites many comparisons, particularly with stories in Scripture. Compare Sleeping Beauty and Eve. How are they alike? How do they differ? Compare the Prince with Christ. How are they alike? How do they differ?

Read Romans 8:18-25. Compare the passage with "Sleeping Beauty," particularly with the "governesses, maids of honor," and others who were put to sleep by the young fairy. Compare the passage in Romans with the cursed castle.

HANS TEGNER, 1900

THE EMPEROR'S NEW SUIT

By Hans Christian Andersen

◆ ◆ ◆

This brief tale, also known by the similar title "The Emperor's New Clothes," was penned by Danish storyteller Hans Christian Andersen and was originally published in 1837, along with "The Little Mermaid." Several older versions of the story may have influenced Andersen's tale, though that cannot be proven. Like many fairy tales, variations of "The Emperor's New Suit" have been told in multiple countries and languages over many centuries. To this day, the tale remains a simple yet profound exploration of courage, hypocrisy, and honesty.

THE TALE

Many, many years ago lived an emperor, who thought so much of new clothes that he spent all his money in order to obtain them; his only ambition was to be always well dressed. He did not care for his soldiers, and the theater did not amuse him; the only thing, in fact, he thought anything of was to drive out and show a new suit of clothes. He had a coat for every hour of the day; and as one would say of a king, "He is in his cabinet," so one could say of him, "The emperor is in his dressing-room."

The great city where he resided was very gay; every day many strangers from all parts of the globe arrived. One day two swindlers came to this city; they made people believe that they were weavers, and declared they could manufacture the finest cloth to be imagined. Their colours and patterns, they said, were not only exceptionally beautiful, but the clothes made of their material possessed the wonderful quality of being invisible to any man who was unfit for his office or unpardonably stupid.

"That must be wonderful cloth," thought the emperor. "If I were to be dressed in a suit made of this cloth, I should be able to find out which men in my empire were unfit for their places, and I could distinguish the clever from the stupid. I must have this cloth woven for me without delay." And he gave a large sum of money to the swindlers, in advance, that they should set to work without any loss of time. They set up two looms, and pretended to be very hard at work, but they did nothing whatever on the looms. They asked for the finest silk and the most precious gold-cloth; all they got they did away with, and worked at the empty looms till late at night.

DISCUSS AS YOU READ:
HOW WOULD YOU DESCRIBE THE EMPEROR SO FAR? WHY?

"I should very much like to know how they are getting on with the cloth," thought the emperor. But he felt rather uneasy when he remembered that he who was not fit for his office could not see it. Personally, he was of opinion that he had nothing to fear, yet he thought it advisable to send somebody else first to see how matters stood. Everybody in the town knew what a remarkable quality the stuff possessed, and all were anxious to see how bad or stupid their neighbours were.

"I shall send my honest old minister to the weavers," thought the emperor. "He can judge best how the stuff looks, for he is intelligent, and nobody understands his office better than he."

The good old minister went into the room where the swindlers sat before the empty looms. "Heaven preserve us!" he thought, and opened his eyes wide. "I cannot see anything at all!" But he did not say so. Both swindlers requested him to come near, and asked him if he did not admire the exquisite pattern and the beautiful colours, pointing to the empty looms. The poor old minister tried his very best, but he could see nothing, for there was nothing to be seen. "Oh dear," he thought, "can I be so stupid? I should never have thought so, and nobody must know it! Is it possible that I am not fit for my office? No, no, I cannot say that I was unable to see the cloth."

"Now, have you got nothing to say?" said one of the swindlers, while he pretended to be busily weaving.

"Oh, it is very pretty, exceedingly beautiful," replied the old minister, looking through his glasses. "What a beautiful pattern, what brilliant colours! I shall tell the emperor that I like the cloth very much."

"We are pleased to hear that," said the two weavers, and described to him the colours and explained the curious pattern. The old minister listened attentively, that he might relate to the emperor what they said; and so he did.

Now the swindlers asked for more money, silk, and gold-cloth, which they required for weaving. They kept everything for themselves, and not a thread came near the loom, but they continued, as hitherto, to work at the empty looms.

Soon afterwards the emperor sent another honest courtier to the weavers to see how they were getting on, and if the cloth was nearly finished. Like the old minister, he looked and looked but could see nothing, as there was nothing to be seen.

"Is it not a beautiful piece of cloth?" asked the two swindlers, showing and explaining the magnificent pattern, which, however, did not exist.

"I am not stupid," said the man. "It is therefore my good appointment for which I am not fit. It is very strange, but I must not let any one know it." And he praised the cloth, which he did not see, and expressed his joy at the beautiful colours and the fine pattern. "It is very excellent," he said to the emperor.

DISCUSS AS YOU READ:
WHAT WORD IS USED TO DESCRIBE THE OLD MINISTER AND THE COURTIER? HOW DO THEY RESPOND WHEN VIEWING THE MAGIC THREAD? WHY DO THEY RESPOND THAT WAY?

Everybody in the whole town talked about the precious cloth. At last the emperor wished to see it himself, while it was still on the loom. With a number of courtiers, including the two who had already been there, he went to the two clever swindlers, who now worked as hard as they could, but without using any thread.

"Is it not magnificent?" said the two old statesmen who had been there before. "Your Majesty must admire the colours and the pattern." And then they pointed to the empty looms, for they imagined the others could see the cloth.

"What is this?" thought the emperor. "I do not see anything at all. That is terrible! Am I stupid? Am I unfit to be emperor? That would indeed be the most dreadful thing that could happen to me."

DISCUSS AS YOU READ:
WHAT DO YOU THINK THE EMPEROR SHOULD DO?

"Really," he said, turning to the weavers, "your cloth has our most gracious approval." And nodding contentedly he looked at the empty loom, for he did not like to say that he saw nothing. All his attendants, who were with him, looked and looked, and although they could not see anything more than the others, they said, like the emperor, "It is very beautiful." And all advised him to wear the new magnificent clothes at a great procession which was soon to take place. "It is magnificent, beautiful, excellent," one heard them say; everybody seemed to be delighted, and the emperor appointed the two swindlers "Imperial Court Weavers."

The whole night previous to the day on which the procession was to take place, the swindlers pretended to work, and burned more than sixteen candles. People should see that they were busy to finish the emperor's new suit. They pretended to take the cloth from the loom, and worked about in the air with big scissors, and sewed with needles without thread, and said at last: "The emperor's new suit is ready now."

The emperor and all his barons then came to the hall; the swindlers held their arms up as if they held something in their hands and said: "These are the trousers!" "This is the coat!" and "Here is the cloak!" and so on. "They are all as light as a cobweb, and one must feel as if one had nothing at all upon the body; but that is just the beauty of them."

"Indeed!" said all the courtiers; but they could not see anything, for there was nothing to be seen.

"Does it please your Majesty now to graciously undress," said the swindlers, "that we may assist your Majesty in putting on the new suit before the large looking-glass?"

The emperor undressed, and the swindlers pretended to put the new suit upon him, one piece after another; and the emperor looked at himself in the glass from every side.

"How well they look! How well they fit!" said all. "What a beautiful pattern! What fine colours! That is a magnificent suit of clothes!"

The master of the ceremonies announced that the bearers of the canopy, which was to be carried in the procession, were ready.

"I am ready," said the emperor. "Does not my suit fit me marvelously?" Then he turned once more to the looking-glass, that people should think he admired his garments.

The chamberlains, who were to carry the train, stretched their hands to the ground as if they lifted up a train, and pretended to hold something in their hands; they did not like people to know that they could not see anything.

The emperor marched in the procession under the beautiful canopy, and all who saw him in the street and out of the windows exclaimed: "Indeed, the emperor's new suit is incomparable! What a long train he has! How well it fits him!" Nobody wished to let others know he saw nothing, for then he would have been unfit for his office or too stupid. Never emperor's clothes were more admired.

"But he has nothing on at all," said a little child at last.

"Good heavens! listen to the voice of an innocent child," said the father, and one whispered to the other what the child had said.

"But he has nothing on at all," cried at last the whole people. That made a deep impression upon the emperor, for it seemed to him that they were right; but he thought to himself, "Now I must bear up to the end." And the chamberlains walked with still greater dignity, as if they carried the train which did not exist.

THE DISCUSSION

First, briefly narrate the story back.

Questions to ask after reading the story:
- How does the ending make you feel? Why does the ending make you feel that way?
- If you could change the ending to this story, what ending would you give it? Why?
- Compare the little child at the end of the story with the emperor. How are they alike? How are they different?
- Appearances are very important in this story. Which characters were most concerned about how they appeared? Why were they so concerned?
- Why do you think the emperor continued the procession to the end?
- Do the characters remind you of characters from any other story? Explain.

Listening for Echoes
Read Matthew 19:13-22 and compare it with "The Emperor's New Suit." How are they similar? How are they different?

THUMBELINA

By Hans Christian Andersen

◆ ◆ ◆

The story of "Thumbelina" was written by Hans Christian Andersen and first published in 1835. The story is his own invention, although he was likely influenced by other similar stories. At the end of the story itself, he explains that he heard the whole thing from the singing swallow that helps Thumbelina. Like "The Princess and the Pea," the scholars and critics of Andersen's day did not like this story of his. They thought that it was told too informally, and that it didn't have a clear enough moral. The story is about a tiny, beautiful girl who is constantly taken by other characters who want to have her as their wife.

THE TALE

There was once a woman who wished very much to have a little child, but she could not obtain her wish. At last she went to a fairy, and said, "I should so very much like to have a little child; can you tell me where I can find one?"

"Oh, that can be easily managed," said the fairy. "Here is a barleycorn of a different kind to those which grow in the farmer's fields, and which the chickens eat; put it into a flower-pot, and see what will happen."

"Thank you," said the woman, and she gave the fairy twelve shillings, which was the price of the barleycorn. Then she went home and planted it, and immediately there grew up a large handsome flower, something like a tulip in appearance, but with its leaves tightly closed as if it were still a bud. "It is a beautiful flower," said the woman, and she kissed the red and golden-colored leaves, and while she did so the flower opened, and she could see that it was a real tulip. Within the flower, upon the green velvet stamens, sat a very delicate and graceful little maiden. She was scarcely half as long as a thumb, and they gave her the name of "Thumbelina," or Tiny, because she was so small. A walnut-shell, elegantly polished, served her for a cradle; her bed was formed of blue violet-leaves, with a rose-leaf for a counterpane. Here she slept at night, but during the day she amused herself on a table, where the woman had placed a plateful of water. Round this plate were wreaths of flowers with their stems in the water, and upon it floated a large tulip-leaf, which served Tiny for a boat. Here the little maiden sat and rowed herself from side to side, with two oars made of white horse-hair. It really was a very pretty sight. Tiny could, also, sing so softly and sweetly that nothing like her singing had ever before been heard. One night, while she lay in her pretty bed, a large, ugly, wet toad crept through a broken pane of glass in the window, and leaped right upon the table where Tiny lay sleeping under her rose-leaf quilt.

"What a pretty little wife this would make for my son," said the toad, and she took up the walnut-shell in which little Tiny lay asleep, and jumped through the window with it into the garden.

In the swampy margin of a broad stream in the garden lived the toad, with her son. He was uglier even than his mother, and when he saw the pretty little maiden in her elegant bed, he could only cry, "Croak, croak, croak."

"Don't speak so loud, or she will wake," said the toad, "and then she might run away, for she is as light as swan's down. We will place her on one of the water-lily leaves out in the stream; it will be like an island to her, she is so light and small, and then she cannot escape; and, while she is away, we will make haste and prepare the state-room under the marsh, in which you are to live when you are married."

Far out in the stream grew a number of water-lilies, with broad green leaves, which seemed to float on the top of the water. The largest of these leaves appeared farther off than the rest, and the old toad swam out to it with the walnut-shell, in which little Tiny lay still asleep. The tiny little creature woke very early in the morning and began to cry bitterly when she found where she was, for she could see nothing but water on every side of the large green leaf, and no way of reaching the land. Meanwhile the old toad was very busy under the marsh, decking her room with rushes and wild yellow flowers, to make it look pretty for her new daughter-in-law. Then she swam out with her ugly son to the leaf on which she had placed poor little Tiny. She wanted to fetch the pretty bed, that she might put it in the bridal chamber to be ready for her. The old toad bowed low to her in the water, and said, "Here is my son, he will be your husband, and you will live happily in the marsh by the stream."

"Croak, croak, croak," was all her son could say for himself; so the toad took up the elegant little bed, and swam away with it, leaving Tiny all alone on the green leaf, where she sat and wept. She could not bear to think of living with the old toad, and having her ugly son for a husband. The little fishes, who swam about in the water beneath, had seen the toad, and heard what she said, so they lifted their heads above the water to look at the little maiden. As soon as they caught sight of her, they saw she was very pretty, and it made them very sorry to think that she must go and live with the ugly toads. "No, it must never be!" so they assembled together in the water, round the green stalk which held the leaf on which the little maiden stood, and gnawed it away at the root with their teeth. Then the leaf floated down the stream, carrying Tiny far away out of reach of land.

Tiny sailed past many towns, and the little birds in the bushes saw her, and sang, "What a lovely little creature." So the leaf swam away with her farther and farther, till it brought her to other lands. A graceful little white butterfly constantly fluttered round her, and at last alighted on the leaf. Tiny pleased him, and she was glad of it, for now the toad could not possibly reach her, and the country through which she sailed was beautiful, and the sun shone upon the water, till it glittered like liquid gold. She took off her girdle and tied one end of it round the butterfly, and the other end of the ribbon she fastened to the leaf, which now glided on much faster than ever, taking little Tiny with it as she stood. Presently a large cockchafer flew by; the moment he caught sight of her, he seized her round her delicate waist with his claws, and flew with her into a tree. The green leaf floated away on the brook, and the butterfly flew with it, for he was fastened to it, and could not get away.

Oh, how frightened little Tiny felt when the cockchafer flew with her to the tree! But especially was she sorry for the beautiful white butterfly which she had fastened to the leaf, for if he could not free himself he would die of hunger. But the cockchafer did not trouble himself at all about the matter. He seated himself by her side on a large green leaf, gave her some honey from the flowers to eat, and told her she was very pretty, though not in the least like a cockchafer. After a time, all the cockchafers turned up their feelers and said, "She has only two legs! How ugly that looks."

"She has no feelers," said another.

"Her waist is quite slim. Pooh! she is like a human being."

"Oh! She is ugly," said all the lady cockchafers, although Tiny was very pretty. Then the cockchafer who had run away with her, believed all the others when they said she was ugly, and would have nothing more to say to her, and told her she might go where she liked. Then he flew down with her from the tree, and placed her on a daisy, and she wept at the thought that she was so ugly that even the cockchafers would have nothing to say to her. And all the while she was really the loveliest creature that one could imagine, and as tender and delicate as a beautiful rose-leaf.

During the whole summer poor little Tiny lived quite alone in the wide forest. She wove herself a bed with blades of grass, and hung it up under a broad leaf, to protect herself from the rain. She sucked the honey from the flowers for food, and drank the dew from their leaves every morning. So passed away the summer and the autumn, and then came the winter—the long, cold winter. All the birds who had sung to her so sweetly were flown away, and the trees and the flowers had withered. The large clover leaf under the shelter of which she had lived, was now rolled together and shrivelled up, nothing remained but a yellow withered stalk. She felt dreadfully cold, for her clothes were torn, and she was herself so frail and delicate, that poor little Tiny was nearly frozen to death. It began to snow too; and the snowflakes, as they fell upon her, were like a whole shovelful falling upon one of us, for we are tall, but she was only an inch high. Then she wrapped herself up in a dry leaf, but it cracked in the middle and could not keep her warm, and she shivered with cold.

Near the wood in which she had been living lay a corn-field, but the corn had been cut a long time; nothing remained but the bare dry stubble standing up out of the frozen ground. It was to her like struggling through a large wood. Oh, how she shivered with the cold. She came at last to the door of a field-mouse, who had a little den under the corn-stubble. There dwelt the field-mouse in warmth and comfort, with a whole roomful of corn, a kitchen, and a beautiful dining room. Poor little Tiny stood before the door just like a little beggar-girl, and begged for a small piece of barley-corn, for she had been without a morsel to eat for two days.

DISCUSS AS YOU READ:
WILL THE FIELD-MOUSE HELP THUMBELINA?

"You poor little creature," said the field-mouse, who was really a good old field-mouse. "Come into my warm room and dine with me." She was very pleased with Tiny, so she said, "You are quite welcome to stay with me all the winter, if you like; but you must keep my rooms clean and neat, and tell me stories, for I shall like to hear them very much." And Tiny did all the field-mouse asked her, and found herself very comfortable.

"We shall have a visitor soon," said the field-mouse one day. "My neighbor pays me a visit once a week. He is better off than I am; he has large rooms, and wears a beautiful black velvet coat. If you could only have him for a husband, you would be well provided for indeed. But he is blind, so you must tell him some of your prettiest stories."

But Tiny did not feel at all interested about this neighbor, for he was a mole. However, he came and paid his visit dressed in his black velvet coat.

"He is very rich and learned, and his house is twenty times larger than mine," said the field-mouse.

He was rich and learned, no doubt, but he always spoke slightingly of the sun and the pretty flowers, because he had never seen them. Tiny was obliged to sing to him, "Lady-bird, lady-bird, fly away home," and many other pretty songs. And the mole fell in love with her because she had such a sweet voice; but he said nothing yet, for he was very cautious. A short time before, the mole had dug a long passage under the earth, which led from the dwelling of the field-mouse to his own, and here she had permission to walk with Tiny whenever she liked. But he warned them not to be alarmed at the sight of a dead bird which lay in the passage. It was a perfect bird, with a beak and feathers, and could not have been dead long, and was lying just where the mole had made his passage. The mole took a piece of phosphorescent wood in his mouth, and it glittered like fire in the dark; then he went before them to light them through the long, dark passage. When they came to the spot where lay the dead bird, the mole pushed his broad nose through the ceiling, the earth gave way, so that there was a large hole, and the daylight shone into the passage. In the middle of the floor lay a dead swallow, his beautiful wings pulled close to his sides, his feet and his head drawn up under his feathers; the poor bird had evidently died of the cold. It made little Tiny very sad to see it, she did so love the little birds; all the summer they had sung and twittered for her so beautifully. But the mole pushed it aside with his crooked legs, and said, "He will sing no more now. How miserable it must be to be born a little bird! I am thankful that none of my children will ever be birds, for they can do nothing but cry, 'Tweet, tweet,' and always die of hunger in the winter."

"Yes, you may well say that, as a clever man!" exclaimed the field-mouse. "What is the use of his twittering, for when winter comes he must either starve or be frozen to death. Still birds are very high bred."

Tiny said nothing; but when the two others had turned their backs on the bird, she stooped down and stroked aside the soft feathers which covered the head, and kissed the closed eyelids. "Perhaps this was the one who sang to me so sweetly in the summer," she said. "And how much pleasure it gave me, you dear, pretty bird."

The mole now stopped up the hole through which the daylight shone, and then accompanied the lady home. But during the night Tiny could not sleep; so she got out of bed and wove a large, beautiful carpet of hay; then she carried it to the dead bird, and spread it over him, with some down from the flowers which she had found in the field-mouse's room. It was as soft as wool, and she spread some of it on each side of the bird, so that he might lie warmly in the cold earth. "Farewell, you pretty little bird," said she, "farewell; thank you for your delightful singing during the summer, when all the trees were green, and the warm sun shone upon us." Then she laid her head on the bird's breast, but she was alarmed immediately, for it seemed as if something inside the bird went "thump, thump." It was the bird's heart; he was not really dead, only benumbed with the cold, and the warmth had restored him to life. In autumn, all the swallows fly away into warm countries, but if one happens to linger, the cold seizes it, it becomes frozen, and falls down as if dead; it remains where it fell, and the cold snow covers it. Tiny trembled very much; she was quite frightened, for the bird was large, a great deal larger than herself—she was only an inch high. But she took courage, laid the wool more thickly over the poor swallow, and then took a leaf which she had used for her own counterpane and laid it over the head of the poor bird. The next morning she again stole out to see him. He was alive but very weak; he could only open his eyes for a moment to look at Tiny, who stood by holding a piece of decayed wood in her hand, for she had no other lantern.

"Thank you, pretty little maiden," said the sick swallow. "I have been so nicely warmed, that I shall soon regain my strength and be able to fly about again in the warm sunshine."

"Oh," said she, "it is cold out of doors now; it snows and freezes. Stay in your warm bed; I will take care of you."

DISCUSS AS YOU READ:
SHOULD THUMBELINA HELP THE SWALLOW?

Then she brought the swallow some water in a flower-leaf, and after he had drank, he told her that he had wounded one of his wings in a thorn-bush and could not fly as fast as the others, who were soon far away on their journey to warm countries. Then at last he had fallen to the earth, and could remember no more, nor how he came to be where she had found him. The whole winter the swallow remained underground, and Tiny nursed him with care and love. Neither the mole nor the field-mouse knew anything about it, for they did not like swallows. Very soon the spring time came, and the sun warmed the earth. Then the swallow bade farewell to Tiny, and she opened the hole in the ceiling which the mole had made. The sun shone in upon them so beautifully that the swallow asked her if she would go with him; she could sit on his back, he said, and he would fly away with her into the green woods. But Tiny knew it would make the field-mouse very grieved if she left her in that manner, so she said, "No, I cannot."

"Farewell, then, farewell, you good, pretty little maiden," said the swallow; and he flew out into the sunshine.

Tiny looked after him, and the tears rose in her eyes. She was very fond of the poor swallow. "Tweet, tweet," sang the bird, as he flew out into the green woods, and Tiny felt very sad. She was not allowed to go out into the warm sunshine. The corn which had been sown in the field over the house of the field-mouse had grown up high into the air, and formed a thick wood to Tiny, who was only an inch in height.

"You are going to be married, Tiny," said the field-mouse. "My neighbor has asked for you. What good fortune for a poor child like you. Now we will prepare your wedding clothes. They must be both woollen and linen. Nothing must be wanting when you are the mole's wife."

Tiny had to turn the spindle, and the field-mouse hired four spiders, who were to weave day and night. Every evening the mole visited her, and was continually speaking of the time when the summer would be over. Then he would keep his wedding-day with Tiny; but now the heat of the sun was so great that it burned the earth, and made it quite hard, like a stone. As soon, as the summer was over, the wedding should take place. But Tiny was not at all pleased; for she did not like the tiresome mole. Every morning when the sun rose, and every evening when it went down, she would creep out at the door, and as the wind blew aside the ears of corn, so that she could see the blue sky, she thought how beautiful and bright it seemed out there, and wished so much to see her dear swallow again. But he never returned; for by this time he had flown far away into the lovely green forest.

When autumn arrived, Tiny had her outfit quite ready; and the field-mouse said to her, "In four weeks the wedding must take place."

Then Tiny wept, and said she would not marry the disagreeable mole.

"Nonsense," replied the field-mouse. "Now don't be obstinate, or I shall bite you with my white teeth. He is a very handsome mole; the queen herself does not wear more beautiful velvets and furs. His kitchen and cellars are quite full. You ought to be very thankful for such good fortune."

So the wedding-day was fixed, on which the mole was to fetch Tiny away to live with him, deep under the earth, and never again to see the warm sun, because he did not like it. The poor child was very unhappy at the thought of saying farewell to the beautiful sun, and as the field-mouse had given her permission to stand at the door, she went to look at it once more.

"Farewell bright sun," she cried, stretching out her arm towards it; and then she walked a short distance from the house; for the corn had been cut, and only the dry stubble remained in the fields. "Farewell, farewell," she repeated, twining her arm round a little red flower that grew just by her side. "Greet the little swallow from me, if you should see him again."

"Tweet, tweet," sounded over her head suddenly. She looked up, and there was the swallow himself flying close by. As soon as he spied Tiny, he was delighted; and then she told him how unwilling she felt to marry the ugly mole, and to live always beneath the earth, and never to see the bright sun any more. And as she told him she wept.

"Cold winter is coming," said the swallow, "and I am going to fly away into warmer countries. Will you go with me? You can sit on my back, and fasten yourself on with your sash. Then we can fly away from the ugly mole and his gloomy rooms—far away, over the mountains, into warmer countries, where the sun shines more brightly than here; where it is always summer, and the flowers bloom in greater beauty. Fly now with me, dear little Tiny; you saved my life when I lay frozen in that dark passage."

"Yes, I will go with you," said Tiny; and she seated herself on the bird's back, with her feet on his outstretched wings, and tied her girdle to one of his strongest feathers.

Then the swallow rose in the air and flew over forest and over sea,

---

DISCUSS AS YOU READ:
WHAT WILL THUMBELINA DO?
WILL SHE LEAVE WITH THE SWALLOW THIS TIME?

---

high above the highest mountains, covered with eternal snow. Tiny would have been frozen in the cold air, but she crept under the bird's warm feathers, keeping her little head uncovered, so that she might admire the beautiful lands over which they passed. At length they reached the warm countries, where the sun shines brightly, and the sky seems so much higher above the earth. Here, on the hedges, and by the wayside, grew purple, green, and white grapes; lemons and oranges hung from trees in the woods; and the air was fragrant with myrtles and orange blossoms. Beautiful children ran along the country lanes, playing with large gay butterflies; and as the swallow flew farther and farther, every place appeared still more lovely.

At last they came to a blue lake, and by the side of it, shaded by trees of the deepest green, stood a palace of dazzling white marble, built in the olden times. Vines clustered round its lofty pillars, and at the top were many swallows' nests, and one of these was the home of the swallow who carried Tiny.

"This is my house," said the swallow. "But it would not do for you to live there—you would not be comfortable. You must choose for yourself one of those lovely flowers, and I will put you down upon it, and then you shall have everything that you can wish to make you happy."

"That will be delightful," she said, and clapped her little hands for joy.

A large marble pillar lay on the ground, which, in falling, had been broken into three pieces. Between these pieces grew the most beautiful large white flowers; so the swallow flew down with Tiny and placed her on one of the broad leaves. But how surprised she was to see in the middle of the flower, a tiny little man, as white and transparent as if he had been made of crystal! He had a gold crown on his head, and delicate wings at his shoulders, and was not much larger than Tiny herself. He was the angel of the flower; for a tiny man and a tiny woman dwell in every flower; and this was the king of them all.

"Oh, how beautiful he is!" whispered Tiny to the swallow.

The little prince was at first quite frightened at the bird, who was like a giant, compared to such a delicate little creature as himself; but when he saw Tiny, he was delighted, and thought her the prettiest little maiden he had ever seen. He took the gold crown from his head, and placed it on hers, and asked her name, and if she would be his wife, and queen over all the flowers.

This certainly was a very different sort of husband to the son of a toad, or the mole, with black velvet and fur; so she said, "Yes," to the handsome prince. Then all the flowers opened, and out of each came a little lady or a tiny lord, all so pretty it was quite a pleasure to look at them. Each of them brought Tiny a present; but the best gift was a pair of beautiful wings, which had belonged to a large white fly; and they fastened them to Tiny's shoulders, so that she might fly from flower to flower. Then there was much rejoicing, and the little swallow who sat above them, in his nest, was asked to sing a wedding song, which he did as well as he could; but in his heart he felt sad, for he was very fond of Tiny, and would have liked never to part from her again.

"You must not be called Tiny any more," said the spirit of the flowers to her. "It is an ugly name, and you are so very pretty. We will call you Maia."

"Farewell, farewell," said the swallow, with a heavy heart as he left the warm countries to fly back into Denmark. There he had a nest over the window of a house in which dwelt the writer of fairy tales. The swallow sang, "Tweet, tweet," and from his song came the whole story.

The Discussion

....

First, briefly narrate the story back.

Questions to ask after reading the story:
- How does the ending make you feel? Why does the ending make you feel that way?
- Should Thumbelina marry the frog? What about the cockchafer (a stag beetle) or the mole? Why or why not?
- Should Thumbelina go with the swallow the first time? What about the second time? Why or why not?
- Compare the frog, the stag beetle, and the mole. How are they alike? How are they different?
- Why do the stag beetles think Thumbelina is ugly? Why does Thumbelina not want to marry the frog or the mole? How are the stag beetles' reactions to Thumbelina similar to and different from Thumbelina's reactions to the frog and mole?
- Do the characters remind you of characters from any other story? Explain.

Listening for Echoes
What other stories have a character who comes to think he or she is ugly because of the judgments of creatures or people different from him or her? Compare this scene in "Thumbelina" to "The Ugly Duckling" and "Cinderella."

In the Bible, the Church is often compared to or described as the "Bride of Christ." How does the Church know which bridegroom is her true husband? How does Thumbelina know which bridegroom is her true husband?

ARTHUR RACKHAM , 1918

JACK AND THE BEANSTALK

BY ANDREW LANG

◆ ◆ ◆

The story of "Jack and the Beanstalk" is a very old story (perhaps thousands of years old, in fact, told through oral tradition), but it first appears in a published form in England in the eighteenth century. In 1734 it was published as "The Story of Jack Spriggins and the Enchanted Bean," and again in 1807 as "The History of Jack and the Bean-Stalk" in a retelling by noted publisher Benjamin Tabart. The version printed here is from Andrew Lang's *Red Fairy Book*, published in 1890. In recent years it has been retold by the likes of Roald Dahl, *Gilligan's Island*, *The Simpsons*, and *The Magic Schoolbus*. The various versions of the story differ primarily in how much backstory they provide for Jack. Those that present Jack as the son of the original owner of the castle, as in the Lang version, clearly see him as the tale's protagonist. But in versions that do not reveal Jack's relationship to the castle, he is sometimes seen negatively, even as a thief and robber. This seeming contradiction attests to the tale's enduring legacy.

THE TALE

JACK SELLS THE COW

Once upon a time there was a poor widow who lived in a little cottage with her only son, Jack.

Jack was a giddy, thoughtless boy, but very kind-hearted and affectionate. There had been a hard winter, and after it the poor woman had suffered from fever and ague. Jack did no work as yet, and by degrees they grew dreadfully poor. The widow saw that there was no means of keeping Jack and herself from starvation but by selling her cow; so one morning she said to her son, "I am too weak to go myself, Jack, so you must take the cow to market for me, and sell her."

Jack liked going to market to sell the cow very much; but as he was on the way, he met a butcher who had some beautiful beans in his hand. Jack stopped to look at them, and the butcher told the boy that they were of great value, and persuaded the silly lad to sell the cow for these beans.

When he brought them home to his mother instead of the money she expected for her nice cow, she was very vexed and shed many tears, scolding Jack for his folly. He was very sorry, and mother and son went to bed very sadly that night; their last hope seemed gone.

At daybreak Jack rose and went out into the garden. "At least," he thought, "I will sow the wonderful beans. Mother says that they are just common scarlet-runners, and nothing else; but I may as well sow them."

So he took a piece of stick, and made some holes in the ground, and put in the beans. That day they had very little dinner, and went sadly to bed, knowing that for the next day there would be none and Jack, unable to sleep from grief and vexation, got up at day-dawn and went out into the garden.

What was his amazement to find that the beans had grown up in the night, and climbed up and up till they covered the high cliff that sheltered the cottage, and disappeared above it! The stalks had twined and twisted themselves together till they formed quite a ladder.

"It would be easy to climb it," thought Jack.

DISCUSS AS YOU READ:
DO YOU THINK JACK WILL CLIMB THE BEANSTALK?

And, having thought of the experiment, he at once resolved to carry it out, for Jack was a good climber. However, after his late mistake about the cow, he thought he had better consult his mother first.

WONDERFUL GROWTH OF THE BEANSTALK

So Jack called his mother, and they both gazed in silent wonder at the Beanstalk, which was not only of great height, but was thick enough to bear Jack's weight.

"I wonder where it ends," said Jack to his mother. "I think I will climb up and see."

His mother wished him not to venture up this strange ladder, but Jack coaxed her to give her consent to the attempt, for he was certain there must be something wonderful in the Beanstalk; so at last she yielded to his wishes.

Jack instantly began to climb, and went up and up on the ladder-like bean till everything he had left behind him—the cottage, the village, and even the tall church tower—looked quite little, and still he could not see the top of the Beanstalk.

Jack felt a little tired, and thought for a moment that he would go back again; but he was a very persevering boy, and he knew that the way to succeed in anything is not to give up. So after resting for a moment he went on.

After climbing higher and higher, till he grew afraid to look down for fear he should be giddy, Jack at last reached the top of the Beanstalk, and found himself in a beautiful country, finely wooded, with beautiful meadows covered with sheep. A crystal stream ran through the pastures; not far from the place where he had got off the Beanstalk stood a fine, strong castle.

Jack wondered very much that he had never heard of or seen this castle before; but when he reflected on the subject, he saw that it was as much separated from the village by the perpendicular rock on which it stood as if it were in another land.

While Jack was standing looking at the castle, a very strange-looking woman came out of the wood, and advanced towards him.

She wore a pointed cap of quilted red satin turned up with ermine, her hair streamed loose over her shoulders, and she walked with a staff. Jack took off his cap and made her a bow. "If you please, ma'am," said he, "is this your house?"

"No," said the old lady. "Listen, and I will tell you the story of that castle.

"Once upon a time there was a noble knight, who lived in this castle, which is on the borders of Fairyland. He had a fair and beloved wife and several lovely children; and as his neighbours, the little people, were very friendly towards him, they bestowed on him many excellent and precious gifts.

"Rumour whispered of these treasures; and a monstrous giant, who lived at no great distance, and who was a very wicked being, resolved to obtain possession of them.

"So he bribed a false servant to let him inside the castle, when the knight was in bed and asleep, and he killed him as he lay. Then he went to the part of the castle which was the nursery, and also killed all the poor little ones he found there.

"Happily for her, the lady was not to be found. She had gone with her infant son, who was only two or three months old, to visit her old nurse, who lived in the valley; and she had been detained all night there by a storm.

"The next morning, as soon as it was light, one of the servants at the castle, who had managed to escape, came to tell the poor lady of the sad fate of her husband and her pretty babes. She could scarcely believe him at first, and was eager at once to go back and share the fate of her dear ones; but the old nurse, with many tears, besought her to remember that she had still a child, and that it was her duty to preserve her life for the sake of the poor innocent.

"The lady yielded to this reasoning, and consented to remain at her nurse's house as the best place of concealment; for the servant told her that the giant had vowed, if he could find her, he would kill both her and her baby. Years rolled on. The old nurse died, leaving her cottage and the few articles of furniture it contained to her poor lady, who dwelt in it, working as a peasant for her daily bread. Her spinning-wheel and the milk of a cow, which she had purchased with the little money she had with her, sufficed for the scanty subsistence of herself and her little son. There was a nice little garden attached to the cottage, in which they cultivated peas, beans, and cabbages, and the lady was not ashamed to go out at harvest time, and glean in the fields to supply her little son's wants.

"Jack, that poor lady is your mother. This castle was once your father's, and must again be yours."

Jack uttered a cry of surprise.

"My mother! Oh, madam, what ought I to do? My poor father! My dear mother!"

"Your duty requires you to win it back for your mother. But the task is a very difficult one, and full of peril, Jack. Have you courage to undertake it?"

"I fear nothing when I am doing right," said Jack.

"Then," said the lady in the red cap, "you are one of those who slay giants. You must get into the castle, and if possible possess yourself of a hen that lays golden eggs, and a harp that talks. Remember, all the giant possesses is really yours." As she ceased speaking, the lady of the red hat suddenly disappeared, and of course Jack knew she was a fairy.

Jack determined at once to attempt the adventure; so he advanced, and blew the horn which hung at the castle portal. The door was opened in a minute or two by a frightful giantess, with one great eye in the middle of her forehead.

As soon as Jack saw her he turned to run away, but she caught him, and dragged him into the castle.

"Ho, ho!" she laughed terribly. "You didn't expect to see me here, that is clear! No, I shan't let you go again. I am weary of my life. I am so overworked, and I don't see why I should not have a page as well as other ladies. And you shall be my boy. You shall clean the knives, and black the boots, and make the fires, and help me generally when the giant is out. When he is at home I must hide you, for he has eaten up all my pages hitherto, and you would be a dainty morsel, my little lad."

While she spoke she dragged Jack right into the castle. The poor boy was very much frightened, as I am sure you and I would have been in his place. But he remembered that fear disgraces a man; so he struggled to be brave and make the best of things.

"I am quite ready to help you, and do all I can to serve you, madam," he said, "only I beg you will be good enough to hide me from your husband, for I should not like to be eaten at all."

"That's a good boy," said the Giantess, nodding her head. "It is lucky for you that you did not scream out when you saw me, as the other boys who have been here did, for if you had done so my husband would have awakened and have eaten you, as he did them, for breakfast. Come here, child; go into my wardrobe: he never ventures to open that; you will be safe there."

And she opened a huge wardrobe which stood in the great hall, and shut him into it. But the keyhole was so large that it admitted plenty of air, and he could see everything that took place through it. By-and-by he heard a heavy tramp on the stairs, like the lumbering along of a great cannon, and then a voice like thunder cried out,

"Fe, fa, fi-fo-fum,
I smell the breath of an Englishman.
Let him be alive or let him be dead,
I'll grind his bones to make my bread."

"Wife," cried the Giant, "there is a man in the castle. Let me have him for breakfast."

"You are grown old and stupid," cried the lady in her loud tones. "It is only a nice fresh steak off an elephant, that I have cooked for you, which you smell. There, sit down and make a good breakfast."

And she placed a huge dish before him of savoury steaming meat, which greatly pleased him, and made him forget his idea of an Englishman being in the castle. When he had breakfasted he went out for a walk; and then the Giantess opened the door, and made Jack come out to help her. He helped her all day. She fed him well, and when evening came put him back in the wardrobe.

THE HEN THAT LAYS GOLDEN EGGS

The Giant came in to supper. Jack watched him through the keyhole, and was amazed to see him pick a wolf's bone, and put half a fowl at a time into his capacious mouth.

When the supper was ended he bade his wife bring him his hen that laid the golden eggs. "It lays as well as it did when it belonged to that paltry knight," he said. "Indeed I think the eggs are heavier than ever."

The Giantess went away, and soon returned with a little brown hen, which she placed on the table before her husband. "And now, my dear," she said, "I am going for a walk, if you don't want me any longer."

"Go," said the Giant. "I shall be glad to have a nap by-and-by."

Then he took up the brown hen and said to her, "Lay!" And she instantly laid a golden egg.

"Lay!" said the Giant again. And she laid another.

"Lay!" he repeated the third time. And again a golden egg lay on the table.

Now Jack was sure this hen was that of which the fairy had spoken.

By-and-by the Giant put the hen down on the floor, and soon after went fast asleep, snoring so loud that it sounded like thunder.

Directly Jack perceived that the Giant was fast asleep, he pushed open the door of the wardrobe and crept out; very softly he stole across the room, and, picking up the hen, made haste to quit the apartment. He knew the way to the kitchen, the door of which he found was left ajar; he opened it, shut and locked it after him, and flew back to the Beanstalk, which he descended as fast as his feet would move.

When his mother saw him enter the house she wept for joy, for she had feared that the fairies had carried him away, or that the Giant had found him. But Jack put the brown hen down before her, and told her how he had been in the Giant's castle, and all his adventures. She was very glad to see the hen, which would make them rich once more.

DISCUSS AS YOU READ:
WILL JACK CLIMB THE BEANSTALK AGAIN?

THE MONEY BAGS

Jack made another journey up the Beanstalk to the Giant's castle one day while his mother had gone to market; but first he dyed his hair and disguised himself. The old woman did not know him again, and dragged him in as she had done before, to help her to do the work; but she heard her husband coming, and hid him in the wardrobe, not thinking that it was the same boy who had stolen the hen. She bade him stay quite still there, or the Giant would eat him.

Then the Giant came in saying,

"Fe, fa, fi-fo-fum,
I smell the breath of an Englishman.
Let him be alive or let him be dead,
I'll grind his bones to make my bread."

"Nonsense!" said the wife. "It is only a roasted bullock that I thought would be a tit-bit for your supper; sit down and I will bring it up at once." The Giant sat down, and soon his wife brought up a roasted bullock on a large dish, and they began their supper. Jack was amazed to see them pick the bones of the bullock as if it had been a lark.

As soon as they had finished their meal, the Giantess rose and said, "Now, my dear, with your leave I am going up to my room to finish the story I am reading. If you want me call for me."

"First," answered the Giant, "bring me my money bags, that I may count my golden pieces before I sleep." The Giantess obeyed. She went and soon returned with two large bags over her shoulders, which she put down by her husband.

"There," she said, "that is all that is left of the knight's money. When you have spent it you must go and take another baron's castle."

"That he shan't, if I can help it," thought Jack.

The Giant, when his wife was gone, took out heaps and heaps of golden pieces, and counted them, and put them in piles, till he was tired of the amusement. Then he swept them all back into their bags, and leaning back in his chair fell fast asleep, snoring so loud that no other sound was audible.

Jack stole softly out of the wardrobe, and taking up the bags of money (which were his very own, because the Giant had stolen them from his father), he ran off, and with great difficulty descending the Beanstalk, laid the bags of gold on his mother's table. She had just returned from town, and was crying at not finding Jack.

"There, mother, I have brought you the gold that my father lost."

"Oh, Jack! you are a very good boy, but I wish you would not risk your precious life in the Giant's castle. Tell me how you came to go there again."

And Jack told her all about it.

DISCUSS AS YOU READ:
WILL JACK CLIMB THE BEANSTALK AGAIN?

Jack's mother was very glad to get the money, but she did not like him to run any risk for her. But after a time Jack made up his mind to go again to the Giant's castle.

THE TALKING HARP

So he climbed the Beanstalk once more, and blew the horn at the Giant's gate. The Giantess soon opened the door; she was very stupid, and did not know him again, but she stopped a minute before she took him in. She feared another robbery; but Jack's fresh face looked so innocent that she could not resist him, and so she bade him come in, and again hid him away in the wardrobe.

DISCUSS AS YOU READ:
WILL THE GIANTESS LET JACK INTO THE CASTLE AGAIN?

By-and-by the Giant came home, and as soon as he had crossed the threshold he roared out,

> "Fe, fa, fi-fo-fum,
> I smell the breath of an Englishman.
> Let him be alive or let him be dead,
> I'll grind his bones to make my bread."

"You stupid old Giant," said his wife. "You only smell a nice sheep, which I have grilled for your dinner."

And the Giant sat down, and his wife brought up a whole sheep for his dinner. When he had eaten it all up, he said, "Now bring me my harp, and I will have a little music while you take your walk."

The Giantess obeyed, and returned with a beautiful harp. The framework was all sparkling with diamonds and rubies, and the strings were all of gold.

"This is one of the nicest things I took from the knight," said the Giant. "I am very fond of music, and my harp is a faithful servant."

So he drew the harp towards him, and said, "Play!" And the harp played a very soft, sad air.

"Play something merrier!" said the Giant. And the harp played a merry tune.

"Now play me a lullaby," roared the Giant. And the harp played a sweet lullaby, to the sound of which its master fell asleep.

Then Jack stole softly out of the wardrobe, and went into the huge kitchen to see if the Giantess had gone out; he found no one there, so he went to the door and opened it softly, for he thought he could not do so with the harp in his hand.

Then he entered the Giant's room and seized the harp and ran away with it; but as he jumped over the threshold the harp called out, "MASTER! MASTER!"

And the Giant woke up.

With a tremendous roar he sprang from his seat, and in two strides had reached the door.

But Jack was very nimble. He fled like lightning with the harp, talking to it as he went (for he saw it was a fairy), and telling it he was the son of its old master, the knight.

Still the Giant came on so fast that he was quite close to poor Jack, and had stretched out his great hand to catch him. But, luckily, just at that moment he stepped upon a loose stone, stumbled, and fell flat on the ground, where he lay at his full length.

This accident gave Jack time to get on the Beanstalk and hasten down it; but just as he reached their own garden he beheld the Giant descending after him.

"Mother, mother!" cried Jack. "Make haste and give me the axe."

His mother ran to him with a hatchet in her hand, and Jack with one tremendous blow cut through all the Beanstalks except one.

"Now, mother, stand out of the way!" said he.

THE GIANT BREAKS HIS NECK

Jack's mother shrank back, and it was well she did so, for just as the Giant took hold of the last branch of the Beanstalk, Jack cut the stem quite through and darted from the spot.

Down came the Giant with a terrible crash, and as he fell on his head, he broke his neck, and lay dead at the feet of the woman he had so much injured.

Before Jack and his mother had recovered from their alarm and agitation, a beautiful lady stood before them.

"Jack," said she, "you have acted like a brave knight's son, and deserve to have your inheritance restored to you. Dig a grave and bury the Giant, and then go and kill the Giantess."

"But," said Jack, "I could not kill anyone unless I were fighting with him; and I could not draw my sword upon a woman. Moreover, the Giantess was very kind to me."

The Fairy smiled on Jack.

"I am very much pleased with your generous feeling," she said. "Nevertheless, return to the castle, and act as you will find needful."

Jack asked the Fairy if she would show him the way to the castle, as the Beanstalk was now down. She told him that she would drive him there in her chariot, which was drawn by two peacocks. Jack thanked her, and sat down in the chariot with her.

The Fairy drove him a long distance round, till they reached a village which lay at the bottom of the hill. Here they found a number of miserable-looking men assembled. The Fairy stopped her carriage and addressed them.

"My friends," said she, "the cruel giant who oppressed you and ate up all your flocks and herds is dead, and this young gentleman was the means of your being delivered from him, and is the son of your kind old master, the knight."

The men gave a loud cheer at these words, and pressed forward to say that they would serve Jack as faithfully as they had served his father. The Fairy bade them follow her to the castle, and they marched thither in a body, and Jack blew the horn and demanded admittance.

The old Giantess saw them coming from the turret loop-hole. She was very much frightened, for she guessed that something had happened to her husband; and as she came downstairs very fast she caught her foot in her dress, and fell from the top to the bottom and broke her neck.

When the people outside found that the door was not opened to them, they took crowbars and forced the portal. Nobody was to be seen, but on leaving the hall they found the body of the Giantess at the foot of the stairs.

Thus Jack took possession of the castle. The Fairy went and brought his mother to him, with the hen and the harp. He had the Giantess buried, and endeavoured as much as lay in his power to do right to those whom the Giant had robbed.

Before her departure for fairyland, the Fairy explained to Jack that she had sent the butcher to meet him with the beans, in order to try what sort of lad he was.

"If you had looked at the gigantic Beanstalk and only stupidly wondered about it," she said, "I should have left you where misfortune had placed you, only restoring her cow to your mother. But you showed an inquiring mind, and great courage and enterprise, therefore you deserve to rise; and when you mounted the Beanstalk you climbed the Ladder of Fortune."

She then took her leave of Jack and his mother.

THE DISCUSSION

First, briefly narrate the story back.

Questions to ask after reading the story:
• How does the ending make you feel? Why does the ending make you feel that way?

• Should Jack have traded the cow for the beans? Why or why not?

• Should Jack climb the beanstalk the first time? The second time? The third time? Why or why not?

• Compare Jack and the Giant. How are they alike? How are they different? Compare Jack's mother and the Giantess. How are they alike? How are they different?

• Is Jack brave or is he foolish? What makes Jack one and not the other? How do we know the difference?

• Do the characters remind you of characters from any other story? Explain.

Listening for Echoes
What other stories have a character who must face a villain that is far more powerful than he is? How do the characters show bravery in those stories? Are their demonstrations of bravery similar to or different from Jack's?

In the Bible, the Israelites face a giant and are unwilling to take him on in battle until the young shepherd boy and future king, David, comes along. How are Jack and David similar and different? How are the Giant and Goliath similar and different?

THEO VAN HOYTEMA, 1893

THE UGLY DUCKLING

BY HANS CHRISTIAN ANDERSEN

◆ ◆ ◆

When first published in 1843, Hans Christian Andersen's original tale "The Ugly Duckling" was greeted with great applause. The story is one of transformation and the search for place, and Andersen once acknowledged that it was a "reflection" of his own life. Not surprisingly, "The Ugly Duckling" is one of the relatively few tales that finds no direct connection to another story. It is, in a sense, one of the few "original" fairy tales.

THE TALE

....

It was lovely summer weather in the country, and the golden corn, the green oats, and the haystacks piled up in the meadows looked beautiful. The stork walking about on his long red legs chattered in the Egyptian language, which he had learnt from his mother. The corn-fields and meadows were surrounded by large forests, in the midst of which were deep pools. It was, indeed, delightful to walk about in the country. In a sunny spot stood a pleasant old farm-house close by a deep river, and from the house down to the water side grew great burdock leaves, so high that under the tallest of them a little child could stand upright. The spot was as wild as the centre of a thick wood. In this snug retreat sat a duck on her nest, watching for her young brood to hatch; she was beginning to get tired of her task, for the little ones were a long time coming out of their shells, and she seldom had any visitors. The other ducks liked much better to swim about in the river than to climb the slippery banks and sit under a burdock leaf to have a gossip with her. At length one shell cracked, and then another, and from each egg came a living creature that lifted its head and cried, "Peep, peep."

"Quack, quack," said the mother, and then they all quacked as well as they could, and looked about them on every side at the large green leaves. Their mother allowed them to look as much as they liked, because green is good for the eyes.

"How large the world is," said the young ducks, when they found how much more room they now had than while they were inside the egg-shell.

"Do you imagine this is the whole world?" asked the mother. "Wait till you have seen the garden; it stretches far beyond that to the parson's field, but I have never ventured to such a distance. Are you all out?" she continued, rising. "No, I declare, the largest egg lies there still. I wonder how long this is to last, I am quite tired of it." And she seated herself again on the nest.

"Well, how are you getting on?" asked an old duck, who paid her a visit.

"One egg is not hatched yet," said the duck. "It will not break. But just look at all the others, are they not the prettiest little ducklings you ever saw? They are the image of their father, who is so unkind, he never comes to see."

"Let me see the egg that will not break," said the duck. "I have no doubt it is a turkey's egg. I was persuaded to hatch some once, and after all my care and trouble with the young ones, they were afraid of the water. I quacked and clucked, but all to no purpose. I could not get them to venture in. Let me look at the egg. Yes, that is a turkey's egg; take my advice, leave it where it is and teach the other children to swim."

"I think I will sit on it a little while longer," said the duck. "As I have sat so long already, a few days will be nothing."

"Please yourself," said the old duck, and she went away.

At last the large egg broke, and a young one crept forth crying, "Peep, peep." It was very large and ugly. The duck stared at it and exclaimed, "It is very large and not at all like the others. I wonder if it really is a turkey. We shall soon find it out, however, when we go to the water. It must go in, if I have to push it myself."

On the next day the weather was delightful and the sun shone brightly on the green burdock leaves, so the mother duck took her young brood down to the water, and jumped in with a splash. "Quack,

quack," cried she, and one after another the little ducklings jumped in. The water closed over their heads, but they came up again in an instant, and swam about quite prettily with their legs paddling under them as easily as possible, and the ugly duckling was also in the water swimming with them.

"Oh," said the mother, "that is not a turkey; how well he uses his legs, and how upright he holds himself! He is my own child, and he is not so very ugly after all if you look at him properly. Quack, quack! come with me now, I will take you into grand society, and introduce you to the farmyard, but you must keep close to me or you may be trodden upon; and, above all, beware of the cat."

When they reached the farmyard, there was a great disturbance: Two families were fighting for an eel's head, which, after all, was carried off by the cat. "See, children, that is the way of the world," said the mother duck, whetting her beak, for she would have liked the eel's head herself. "Come, now, use your legs, and let me see how well you can behave. You must bow your heads prettily to that old duck yonder; she is the highest born of them all, and has Spanish blood; therefore, she is well off. Don't you see she has a red flag tied to her leg, which is something very grand, and a great honor for a duck; it shows that every one is anxious not to lose her, as she can be recognized both by man and beast. Come, now, don't turn your toes; a well-bred duckling spreads his feet wide apart, just like his father and mother, in this way; now bend your neck, and say 'quack.'"

The ducklings did as they were bid, but the other duck stared, and said, "Look, here comes another brood, as if there were not enough of us already! And what a queer looking object one of them is; we don't want him here." And then one flew out and bit him in the neck.

"Let him alone," said the mother, "he is not doing any harm."

"Yes, but he is so big and ugly," said the spiteful duck, "and therefore he must be turned out."

"The others are very pretty children," said the old duck, with the rag on her leg. "All but that one; I wish his mother could improve him a little."

"That is impossible, your grace," replied the mother. "He is not pretty; but he has a very good disposition, and swims as well or even better than the others. I think he will grow up pretty, and perhaps be smaller; he has remained too long in the egg, and therefore his figure is not properly formed." And then she stroked his neck and smoothed the feathers, saying, "It is a drake, and therefore not of so much consequence. I think he will grow up strong, and able to take care of himself."

"The other ducklings are graceful enough," said the old duck. "Now make yourself at home, and if you can find an eel's head, you can bring it to me."

And so they made themselves comfortable; but the poor duckling, who had crept out of his shell last of all, and looked so ugly, was bitten and pushed and made fun of, not only by the ducks, but by all the poultry. "He is too big," they all said, and the turkey cock, who had been born into the world with spurs, and fancied himself really an emperor, puffed himself out like a vessel in full sail, and flew at the duckling, and became quite red in the head with passion, so that the poor little thing did not know where to go and was quite miserable because he was so ugly and laughed at by the whole farmyard. So it went on from day to day till it got worse and worse.

The poor duckling was driven about by every one; even his brothers and sisters were unkind to him and would say, "Ah, you ugly creature, I wish the cat would get you," and his mother said she wished he had never been born. The ducks pecked him, the chickens beat him, and the girl who fed the poultry kicked him with her feet. So at last he ran away, frightening the little birds in the hedge as he flew over the palings.

"They are afraid of me because I am ugly," he said. So he closed his eyes, and flew still farther, until he came out on a large moor, inhabited by wild ducks. Here he remained the whole night, feeling very tired and sorrowful.

In the morning, when the wild ducks rose in the air, they stared at their new comrade. "What sort of a duck are you?" they all said, coming round him. He bowed to them, and was as polite as he could be, but

---

DISCUSS AS YOU READ:
WHY DID THE DUCKLING LEAVE?
DO YOU THINK HE SHOULD HAVE LEFT?

---

he did not reply to their question.

"You are exceedingly ugly," said the wild ducks, "but that will not matter if you do not want to marry one of our family."

Poor thing! He had no thoughts of marriage; all he wanted was permission to lie among the rushes and drink some of the water on the moor. After he had been on the moor two days, there came two wild geese, or rather goslings, for they had not been out of the egg long, and were very saucy. "Listen, friend," said one of them to the duckling, "you are so ugly that we like you very well. Will you go with us, and become a bird of passage? Not far from here is another moor, in which there are some pretty wild geese, all unmarried. It is a chance for you to get a wife; you may be lucky, ugly as you are."

"Pop, pop," sounded in the air, and the two wild geese fell dead among the rushes, and the water was tinged with blood. "Pop, pop," echoed far and wide in the distance, and whole flocks of wild geese rose up from the rushes. The sound continued from every direction, for the sportsmen surrounded the moor, and some were even seated on branches of trees, overlooking the rushes. The blue smoke from the guns rose like clouds over the dark trees, and as it floated away across the water, a number of sporting dogs bounded in among the rushes, which bent beneath them wherever they went. How they terrified the poor duckling!

He turned away his head to hide it under his wing, and at the same moment a large terrible dog passed quite near him. His jaws were open, his tongue hung from his mouth, and his eyes glared fearfully. He thrust his nose close to the duckling, showing his sharp teeth, and then, "splash, splash," he went into the water without touching him. "Oh," sighed the duckling, "how thankful I am for being so ugly; even a dog will not bite me." And so he lay quite still, while the shot rattled through the rushes, and gun after gun was fired over him. It was late in the day before all became quiet, but even then the poor young thing did not dare to move. He waited quietly for several hours, and then, after looking carefully around him, hastened away from the moor as fast as he could.

He ran over field and meadow till a storm arose, and he could hardly struggle against it. Towards evening, he reached a poor little cottage that seemed ready to fall, and only remained standing because it could not decide on which side to fall first. The storm continued so violent, that the duckling could go no farther; he sat down by the cottage, and then he noticed that the door was not quite closed in consequence of one of the hinges having given way. There was therefore a narrow opening near the bottom large enough for him to slip through, which he did very quietly, and got a shelter for the night. A woman, a tom cat, and a hen lived in this cottage. The tom cat, whom the mistress called "My little son," was a great favorite; he could raise his back, and purr, and could even throw out sparks from his fur if it were stroked the wrong way. The hen had very short legs, so she was called "Chickie short legs." She laid good eggs, and her mistress loved her as if she had been her own child. In the morning, the strange visitor was discovered, and the tom cat began to purr, and the hen to cluck.

"What is that noise about?" said the old woman, looking round the room, but her sight was not very good; therefore, when she saw the duckling she thought it must be a fat duck, that had strayed from home. "Oh what a prize!" she exclaimed, "I hope it is not a drake, for then I shall have some duck's eggs. I must wait and see." So the duck-ling was allowed to remain on trial for three weeks, but there were no eggs. Now the tom cat was the master of the house, and the hen was mistress, and they always said, "We and the world," for they believed themselves to be half the world, and the better half too. The duckling thought that others might hold a different opinion on the subject, but the hen would not listen to such doubts.

"Can you lay eggs?" she asked.

"No."

"Then have the goodness to hold your tongue."

"Can you raise your back, or purr, or throw out sparks?" said the tom cat.

"No."

"Then you have no right to express an opinion when sensible people are speaking."

So the duckling sat in a corner, feeling very low spirited, till the sunshine and the fresh air came into the room through the open door, and then he began to feel such a great longing for a swim on the water, that he could not help telling the hen.

"What an absurd idea," said the hen. "You have nothing else to do, therefore you have foolish fancies. If you could purr or lay eggs, they would pass away."

"But it is so delightful to swim about on the water," said the duckling, "and so refreshing to feel it close over your head, while you dive down to the bottom."

"Delightful, indeed!" said the hen. "Why, you must be crazy! Ask the cat, he is the cleverest animal I know, ask him how he would like to swim about on the water, or to dive under it, for I will not speak of my own opinion; ask our mistress, the old woman—there is no one in the world more clever than she is. Do you think she would like to swim, or to let the water close over her head?"

"You don't understand me," said the duckling.

"We don't understand you? Who can understand you, I wonder? Do you consider yourself more clever than the cat, or the old woman? I will say nothing of myself. Don't imagine such nonsense, child, and thank your good fortune that you have been received here. Are you not in a warm room, and in society from which you may learn something? But you are a chatterer, and your company is not very agreeable. Believe me, I speak only for your own good. I may tell you unpleasant truths, but that is a proof of my friendship. I advise you, therefore, to lay eggs, and learn to purr as quickly as possible."

"I believe I must go out into the world again," said the duckling.

DISCUSS AS YOU READ:
WHY DOESN'T THE DUCKLING FEEL AT HOME
WITH THE OLD WOMAN, THE CAT, AND THE HEN?

"Yes, do," said the hen. So the duckling left the cottage and soon found water on which it could swim and dive, but was avoided by all other animals because of its ugly appearance. Autumn came, and the leaves in the forest turned to orange and gold. Then, as winter approached, the wind caught them as they fell and whirled them in the cold air. The clouds, heavy with hail and snowflakes, hung low in the sky, and the raven stood on the ferns crying, "Croak, croak." It made one shiver with cold to look at him. All this was very sad for the poor little duckling. One evening, just as the sun set amid radiant clouds, there came a large flock of beautiful birds out of the bushes. The duckling had never seen any like them before. They were swans, and they curved their graceful necks, while their soft plumage shown with dazzling whiteness. They uttered a singular cry, as they spread their glorious wings and flew away from those cold regions to warmer countries across the sea. As they mounted higher and higher in the air, the ugly little duckling felt quite a strange sensation as he watched them. He whirled himself in the water like a wheel, stretched out his neck towards them, and uttered a cry so strange that it frightened himself. Could he ever forget those beautiful, happy birds? And when at last they were out of his sight, he dived under the water, and rose again almost beside himself with excitement. He knew not the names of these birds, nor where they had flown, but he felt towards them as he had never felt for any other bird in the world. He was not envious of these

DISCUSS AS YOU READ:
WHAT DOES THE UGLY DUCKLING SEEM
TO WANT MORE THAN ANYTHING ELSE?

beautiful creatures, but wished to be as lovely as they.

Poor ugly creature, how gladly he would have lived even with the ducks, had they only given him encouragement.

The winter grew colder and colder; he was obliged to swim about on the water to keep it from freezing, but every night the space on which he swam became smaller and smaller. At length it froze so hard that the ice in the water crackled as he moved, and the duckling had to paddle with his legs as well as he could to keep the space from closing up. He became exhausted at last, and lay still and helpless, frozen fast in the ice.

Early in the morning, a peasant, who was passing by, saw what had happened. He broke the ice in pieces with his wooden shoe and carried the duckling home to his wife. The warmth revived the poor little creature. But when the children wanted to play with him, the duckling thought they would do him some harm; so he started up in terror, fluttered into the milk-pan, and splashed the milk about the room. Then the woman clapped her hands, which frightened him still more. He flew first into the butter-cask, then into the meal-tub, and out again. What a condition he was in! The woman screamed, and struck at him with the tongs; the children laughed and screamed, and tumbled over each other, in their efforts to catch him; but luckily he escaped. The door stood open; the poor creature could just manage to slip out among the bushes, and lie down quite exhausted in the newly fallen snow.

It would be very sad, were I to relate all the misery and privations which the poor little duckling endured during the hard winter; but when it had passed, he found himself lying one morning in a moor, amongst the rushes. He felt the warm sun shining, and heard the lark singing, and saw that all around was beautiful spring. Then the young bird felt that his wings were strong, as he flapped them against his sides, and rose high into the air. They bore him onwards, until he found himself in a large garden, before he well knew how it had happened.

The apple trees were in full blossom, and the fragrant elders bent their long green branches down to the stream which wound round a smooth lawn. Everything looked beautiful, in the freshness of early spring. From a thicket close by came three beautiful white swans, rustling their feathers, and swimming lightly over the smooth water. The duckling remembered the lovely birds, and felt more strangely unhappy than ever.

"I will fly to those royal birds," he exclaimed, "and they will kill me because I am so ugly and dare to approach them; but it does not matter: better be killed by them than pecked by the ducks, beaten by the hens, pushed about by the maiden who feeds the poultry, or starved with hunger in the winter."

Then he flew to the water, and swam towards the beautiful swans. The moment they espied the stranger, they rushed to meet him with outstretched wings.

"Kill me," said the poor bird; and he bent his head down to the surface of the water, and awaited death.

But what did he see in the clear stream below? His own image; no longer a dark, gray bird, ugly and disagreeable to look at, but a graceful and beautiful swan. To be born in a duck's nest, in a farmyard, is of no consequence to a bird, if it is hatched from a swan's egg. He now felt glad at having suffered sorrow and trouble, because it enabled him to enjoy so much better all the pleasure and happiness around him; for the great swans swam round the new-comer, and stroked his neck with their beaks as a welcome.

Into the garden presently came some little children, and threw bread and cake into the water. "See," cried the youngest, "there is a new one."

And the rest were delighted, and ran to their father and mother, dancing and clapping their hands, and shouting joyously, "There is another swan come; a new one has arrived."

Then they threw more bread and cake into the water and said, "The new one is the most beautiful of all; he is so young and pretty." And the old swans bowed their heads before him.

Then he felt quite ashamed and hid his head under his wing; for he did not know what to do, he was so happy, and yet not at all proud. He had been persecuted and despised for his ugliness, and now he heard them say he was the most beautiful of all the birds. Even the elder tree bent down its bows into the water before him, and the sun shone warm and bright. Then he rustled his feathers, curved his slender neck, and cried joyfully, from the depths of his heart, "I never dreamed of such happiness as this, while I was an ugly duckling."

THE DISCUSSION

....

First, briefly narrate the story back.

Questions to ask after reading the story:
• How does the ending make you feel? Why does the ending make you feel that way?
• Read the first few sentences of the story, particularly noting the adjectives used. How is the farm described? Why might that be important in the story?
• Compare the ugly duckling to his siblings. How are they alike? How are they different?
• Does anyone in the story treat the ugly duckling with kindness? Explain.
• Do the characters remind you of characters from any other story? Explain.

Listening for Echoes
Compare "The Ugly Duckling" and "Cinderella." How are those stories alike? How are they different? How are the duckling and Cinderella alike? How are they different?

EDMUND DULAC, 1911

THE PRINCESS AND THE PEA

By Hans Christian Andersen

◆ ◆ ◆

The story of "The Princess and the Pea" was written by Hans Christian Andersen and first published in 1835, along with three other original Andersen stories. Andersen claimed to have heard a version of the story as a child, but it is not a story traditionally told in Denmark, his native country, and may have been derived from nearby Sweden. Many scholars and critics of Andersen's day did not approve of the story, believing it to be too informal. However, Andersen reputedly developed this conversational style in homage to the oral traditions from which most fairy tales derive, and to counteract the more sophisticated, formal style of the storytellers of his day. Andersen was a true inventor, and this lovely, lasting tale is proof of his capacity to delight readers of all ages.

THE TALE

O nce upon a time there was a prince who wanted to marry a princess; but she would have to be a real princess. He traveled all over the world to find one, but nowhere could he get what he wanted. There were princesses enough, but it was difficult to find out whether they were real ones. There was always something about them that was not as it should be. So he came home again and was sad, for he would have liked very much to have a real princess.

One evening a terrible storm came on; there was thunder and lightning, and the rain poured down in torrents. Suddenly a knocking was heard at the city gate, and the old king went to open it.

It was a princess standing out there in front of the gate. But, good gracious! what a sight the rain and the wind had made her look. The water ran down from her hair and clothes; it ran down into the toes of her shoes and out again at the heels. And yet she said that she was a real princess.

"Well, we'll soon find that out," thought the old queen. But she said nothing, went into the bedroom, took all the bedding off the bedstead, and laid a pea on the bottom; then she took twenty mattresses and laid them on the pea, and then twenty eider-down beds on top of

---

DISCUSS AS YOU READ:
DO YOU THINK THE OLD KING WILL INVITE
THE PRINCESS IN OUT OF THE RAIN?

the mattresses.

On this the princess had to lie all night. In the morning she was asked how she had slept.

DISCUSS AS YOU READ:
HOW WILL THE PRINCESS ANSWER THE QUESTION?

"Oh, very badly!" said she. "I have scarcely closed my eyes all night. Heaven only knows what was in the bed, but I was lying on something hard, so that I am black and blue all over my body. It's horrible!"

Now they knew that she was a real princess because she had felt the pea right through the twenty mattresses and the twenty eider-down beds.

Nobody but a real princess could be as sensitive as that.

So the prince took her for his wife, for now he knew that he had a real princess; and the pea was put in the museum, where it may still be seen, if no one has stolen it.

There, that is a true story.

THE DISCUSSION

First, briefly narrate the story back.

Questions to ask after reading the story:
• How does the ending make you feel? Why does the ending make you feel that way?
• Should the queen test the princess? Why or why not?
• Should the princess tell the truth about how she slept? Why or why not?
• Compare the princess in this story to princesses in other stories. How are they alike? How are they different?
• This story is about sensitivity. Is her sensitivity a good or bad thing? Why?
• Why does the princess's sensitivity prove her identity?
• Do the characters remind you of characters from any other story? Explain.

Listening for Echoes
Replace the pea with different things that we dislike (or ought to dislike). What kinds of things would make us more like a prince or princess? What kinds of things make us less like a prince or princess?

How do other characters in this tale prove their identity? How does Tamar prove her identity to her father-in-law in the book of Genesis? How does Odysseus prove his identity to Penelope in the Odyssey? How does Jesus prove his identity to the men traveling to Emmaus near the end of the Gospel of Luke?

LESLIE BROOKE, 1904

THE THREE LITTLE PIGS

By Andrew Lang

♦ ♦ ♦

The story of "The Three Little Pigs" is one of the most beloved (and anthologized) stories ever told. Some scholars believe it originated many centuries ago, although its exact derivation is unknown. The version included here is from Andrew Lang's *Green Fairy Book* (1892), but other popular retellings include James Halliwell-Phillipps' from *The Nursery Rhymes of England* (1886), and Joseph Jacobs' from *English Fairy Tales* (1890). Jacobs' retelling, while not the oldest version, inspired Walt Disney's *Silly Symphony* cartoon from 1933—a much lighter telling than the one Lang shared, and which subsequently became the version with which most children are familiar. In the decades since the Disney cartoon was released, dozens of other adaptations have been produced for television and books, each of which offers its own distinctive take on the traditional tale of three pigs who are under siege by an evil wolf (or, as in the version here, a fox). Lang's telling is set apart by his unique attention to characterization and motive, which most other contemporary versions tend to ignore.

The Tale

There was once upon a time a pig who lived with her three children on a large, comfortable, old-fashioned farmyard. The eldest of the little pigs was called Browny, the second Whitey, and the youngest and best looking Blacky. Now Browny was a very dirty little pig, and I am sorry to say spent most of his time rolling and wallowing about in the mud. He was never so happy as on a wet day, when the mud in the farmyard got soft, and thick, and slab. Then he would steal away from his mother's side, and finding the muddiest place in the yard, would roll about in it and thoroughly enjoy himself. His mother often found fault with him for this, and would shake her head sadly and say: "Ah, Browny! Some day you will be sorry that you did not obey your old mother." But no words of advice or warning could cure Browny of his bad habits.

Whitey was quite a clever little pig, but she was greedy. She was always thinking of her food and looking forward to her dinner; and when the farm girl was seen carrying the pails across the yard, she would rise up on her hind legs and dance and caper with excitement. As soon as the food was poured into the trough she jostled Blacky and Browny out of the way in her eagerness to get the best and biggest bits for herself. Her mother often scolded her for her selfishness, and told her that some day she would suffer for being so greedy and grabbing.

DISCUSS AS YOU READ:
WHY DO YOU THINK BROWNY AND WHITEY WON'T LISTEN TO THEIR MOTHER?

Blacky was a good, nice little pig, neither dirty nor greedy. He had nice dainty ways (for a pig), and his skin was always as smooth and shining as black satin. He was much cleverer than Browny and Whitey, and his mother's heart used to swell with pride when she heard the farmer's friends say to each other that some day the little black fellow would be a prize pig.

Now the time came when the mother pig felt old and feeble and near her end. One day she called the three little pigs round her and said, "My children, I feel that I am growing old and weak, and that I shall not live long. Before I die I should like to build a house for each of you, as this dear old sty in which we have lived so happily will be given to a new family of pigs, and you will have to turn out. Now, Browny, what sort of a house would you like to have?"

"A house of mud," replied Browny, looking longingly at a wet puddle in the corner of the yard.

"And you, Whitey?" said the mother pig in rather a sad voice, for she was disappointed that Browny had made so foolish a choice.

"A house of cabbage," answered Whitey, with a mouth full, and scarcely raising her snout out of the trough in which she was grubbing for some potato-parings.

"Foolish, foolish child!" said the mother pig, looking quite distressed. "And you, Blacky?" turning to her youngest son. "What sort of a house shall I order for you?"

"A house of brick, please mother, as it will be warm in winter, and cool in summer, and safe all the year round."

"That is a sensible little pig," replied his mother, looking fondly at him. "I will see that the three houses are got ready at once. And now one last piece of advice. You have heard me talk of our old enemy the fox. When he hears that I am dead, he is sure to try and get hold of you, to carry you off to his den. He is very sly and will no doubt disguise himself, and pretend to be a friend, but you must promise me not to let him enter your houses on any pretext whatever."

DISCUSS AS YOU READ:
IF YOU WERE THE MOTHER, WHAT WOULD YOU HAVE DONE WHEN THE FIRST TWO LITTLE PIGS FOOLISHLY CHOSE MUD AND CABBAGES TO BUILD THEIR HOUSES?

And the little pigs readily promised, for they had always had a great fear of the fox, of whom they had heard many terrible tales. A short time afterwards the old pig died, and the little pigs went to live in their own houses.

Browny was quite delighted with his soft mud walls and with the clay floor, which soon looked like nothing but a big mud pie. But that was what Browny enjoyed, and he was as happy as possible, rolling about all day and making himself in such a mess. One day, as he was lying half asleep in the mud, he heard a soft knock at his door, and a gentle voice said, "May I come in, Master Browny? I want to see your beautiful new house."

"Who are you?" said Browny, starting up in great fright, for though the voice sounded gentle, he felt sure it was a feigned voice, and he feared it was the fox.

"I am a friend come to call on you," answered the voice.

"No, no," replied Browny, "I don't believe you are a friend. You are the wicked fox, against whom our mother warned us. I won't let you in."

"Oho! Is that the way you answer me?" said the fox, speaking very roughly in his natural voice. "We shall soon see who is master here." And with his paws he set to work and scraped a large hole in the soft mud walls. A moment later he had jumped through it, and catching

Browny by the neck, flung him on his shoulders and trotted off with him to his den.

The next day, as Whitey was munching a few leaves of cabbage out of the corner of her house, the fox stole up to her door, determined to carry her off to join her brother in his den. He began speaking to her in the same feigned gentle voice in which he had spoken to Browny; but it frightened her very much when he said, "I am a friend come to visit you, and to have some of your good cabbage for my dinner."

"Please don't touch it," cried Whitey in great distress. "The cabbages are the walls of my house, and if you eat them you will make a hole, and the wind and rain will come in and give me a cold. Do go away; I am sure you are not a friend, but our wicked enemy the fox." And poor Whitey began to whine and to whimper, and to wish that she had not been such a greedy little pig, and had chosen a more solid material than cabbages for her house. But it was too late now, and in another minute the fox had eaten his way through the cabbage walls, and had caught the trembling, shivering Whitey, and carried her off to his den.

The next day the fox started off for Blacky's house, because he had made up his mind that he would get the three little pigs together in his den, and then kill them, and invite all his friends to a feast. But when he reached the brick house, he found that the door was bolted and barred, so in his sly manner he began, "Do let me in, dear Blacky. I have brought you a present of some eggs that I picked up in a farmyard on my way here."

"No, no, Mister Fox," replied Blacky. "I am not going to open my door to you. I know your cunning ways. You have carried off poor Browny and Whitey, but you are not going to get me."

At this the fox was so angry that he dashed with all his force against the wall, and tried to knock it down. But it was too strong and well-built; and though the fox scraped and tore at the bricks with his paws he only hurt himself, and at last he had to give it up, and limp away with his fore-paws all bleeding and sore.

"Never mind!" he cried angrily as he went off. "I'll catch you another day, see if I don't, and won't I grind your bones to powder when I have got you in my den!" And he snarled fiercely and showed his teeth.

DISCUSS AS YOU READ:
WHAT SHOULD BLACKY DO NOW?

Next day Blacky had to go into the neighbouring town to do some marketing and to buy a big kettle. As he was walking home with it slung over his shoulder, he heard a sound of steps stealthily creeping after him. For a moment his heart stood still with fear, and then a happy thought came to him. He had just reached the top of a hill, and could see his own little house nestling at the foot of it among the trees. In a moment he had snatched the lid off the kettle and had jumped in himself. Coiling himself round he lay quite snug in the bottom of the kettle, while with his fore-leg he managed to put the lid on, so that he was entirely hidden. With a little kick from the inside he started the kettle off, and down the hill it rolled full tilt; and when the fox came up, all that he saw was a large black kettle spinning over the ground at a great pace. Very much disappointed, he was just going to turn away, when he saw the kettle stop close to the little brick house, and in a moment later Blacky jumped out of it and escaped with the kettle into the house, when he barred and bolted the door, and put the shutter up over the window.

"Oho!" exclaimed the fox to himself. "You think you will escape me that way, do you? We shall soon see about that, my friend." And very quietly and stealthily he prowled round the house looking for some way to climb on to the roof.

In the meantime Blacky had filled the kettle with water, and having put it on the fire, sat down quietly waiting for it to boil. Just as the kettle was beginning to sing, and steam to come out of the spout, he heard a sound like a soft, muffled step, "patter, patter, patter" overhead, and the next moment the fox's head and fore-paws were seen coming down the chimney. But Blacky very wisely had not put the lid on the kettle, and, with a yelp of pain, the fox fell into the boiling water, and before he could escape, Blacky had popped the lid on, and the fox was scalded to death.

As soon as he was sure that their wicked enemy was really dead, and could do them no further harm, Blacky started off to rescue Browny and Whitey. As he approached the den he heard piteous grunts and squeals from his poor little brother and sister who lived in constant terror of the fox killing and eating them. But when they saw Blacky appear at the entrance to the den their joy knew no bounds. He quickly found a sharp stone and cut the cords by which they were tied to a stake in the ground, and then all three started off together for Blacky's house, where they lived happily ever after; and Browny quite gave up rolling in the mud, and Whitey ceased to be greedy, for they never forgot how nearly these faults had brought them to an untimely end.

THE DISCUSSION

First, briefly narrate the story back.

Questions to ask after reading the story:
• How does the ending make you feel? Why does the ending make you feel that way?
• Which character in this story is most courageous? Why?
• Do you think Blacky should have let his brother and sister live with him?
• Do you think the fox deserved to die?
• The mother pig says the fox is clever and should be feared. Do you agree?
• Do the characters remind you of characters from any other story? Explain.

Listening for Echoes
How is this version of the story different from the other versions you may have heard? Why do you think so many versions of this story have been told over the years?

Why do you think so many stories are about clever animals trying to escape foxes or wolves?

R. ANNING BELL , 1912

THE GOLDEN GOOSE

By Andrew Lang

◆ ◆ ◆

Although first collected by the Brothers Grimm early in the nine-teenth century, "The Golden Goose" is a classic fairy tale told in some form by most cultures throughout history, including the ancient Greeks and Hindus. The retelling we include here is from Andrew Lang's *Red Fairy Book* (published in 1890), and includes some minor alterations to the Grimm version. In the Grimm tell-ing the protagonist is called either "Dummling" or "Simpleton," depending on the source, whereas in the Lang version his name is Dullhead. Either way, it's clear he's not considered very bright by his family. Ultimately, this beloved fairy tale falls within two folk-lore traditions: that of the magical fowl that somehow saves the down-and-out (see also the Aesop fable, "The Goose That Laid the Golden Egg"), and that of the mysterious magical little man with the power to bless or curse (as in "Rumpelstiltskin").

THE TALE

....

There was once a man who had three sons. The youngest of them was called Dullhead, and was sneered and jeered at and snubbed on every possible opportunity.

One day it happened that the eldest son wished to go into the forest to cut wood, and before he started his mother gave him a fine rich cake and a bottle of wine, so that he might be sure not to suffer from hunger or thirst.

When he reached the forest he met a little old grey man who wished him "Good-morning," and said, "Do give me a piece of that cake you have got in your pocket, and let me have a draught of your wine—I am so hungry and thirsty."

But this clever son replied, "If I give you my cake and wine I shall have none left for myself; you just go your own way." And he left the little man standing there and went further on into the forest. There he began to cut down a tree, but before long he made a false stroke with his axe, and cut his own arm so badly that he was obliged to go home and have it bound up.

Then the second son went to the forest, and his mother gave him a good cake and a bottle of wine as she had to his elder brother. He too met the little old grey man, who begged him for a morsel of cake and a draught of wine.

But the second son spoke most sensibly too, and said, "Whatever I give to you I deprive myself of. Just go your own way, will you?" Not long after, his punishment overtook him, for no sooner had he struck a couple of blows on a tree with his axe, than he cut his leg so badly that he had to be carried home.

So then Dullhead said, "Father, let me go out and cut wood."

But his father answered, "Both your brothers have injured themselves. You had better leave it alone; you know nothing about it."

But Dullhead begged so hard to be allowed to go that at last his father said, "Very well, then—go. Perhaps when you have hurt yourself, you may learn to know better." His mother only gave him a very plain cake made with water and baked in the cinders, and a bottle of sour beer.

When he got to the forest, he too met the little grey old man, who greeted him and said, "Give me a piece of your cake and a draught from your bottle; I am so hungry and thirsty."

And Dullhead replied, "I've only got a cinder-cake and some sour beer, but if you care to have that, let us sit down and eat."

So they sat down, and when Dullhead brought out his cake he found it had turned into a fine rich cake, and the sour beer into excellent wine. Then they ate and drank, and when they had finished, the little man said, "Now I will bring you luck, because you have a kind heart and are willing to share what you have with others. There stands an old tree; cut it down, and amongst its roots you'll find something." With that the little man took leave.

Then Dullhead fell to at once to hew down the tree, and when it fell he found amongst its roots a goose, whose feathers were all of pure gold. He lifted it out, carried it off, and took it with him to an inn where he meant to spend the night.

DISCUSS AS YOU READ:
WHY DOESN'T DULLHEAD GO HOME, AND INSTEAD GO TO AN INN?

Now the landlord of the inn had three daughters, and when they saw the goose they were filled with curiosity as to what this wonderful bird could be, and each longed to have one of its golden feathers.

The eldest thought to herself, "No doubt I shall soon find a good opportunity to pluck out one of its feathers," and the first time Dullhead happened to leave the room she caught hold of the goose by its wing. But, lo and behold! Her fingers seemed to stick fast to the goose, and she could not take her hand away.

Soon after, the second daughter came in, and thought to pluck a golden feather for herself too; but hardly had she touched her sister than she stuck fast as well. At last the third sister came with the same intentions, but the other two cried out, "Keep off! For Heaven's sake, keep off!"

The younger sister could not imagine why she was to keep off, and thought to herself, "If they are both there, why should not I be there too?"

So she sprang to them; but no sooner had she touched one of them than she stuck fast to her. So they all three had to spend the night with the goose.

Next morning Dullhead tucked the goose under his arm and went off, without in the least troubling himself about the three girls who were hanging on to it. They just had to run after him right or left as best they could. In the middle of a field they met the parson, and when he saw this procession he cried, "For shame, you bold girls! What do you mean by running after a young fellow through the fields like that? Do you call that proper behaviour?" And with that he caught the youngest girl by the hand to try and draw her away. But directly he touched her he hung on himself, and had to run along with the rest of them.

Not long after the clerk came that way, and was much surprised to see the parson following the footsteps of three girls. "Why, where is your reverence going so fast?" cried he. "Don't forget there is to be a christening to-day." And he ran after him, caught him by the sleeve, and hung on to it himself. As the five of them trotted along in this fashion one after the other, two peasants were coming from their work with their hoes. On seeing them the parson called out and begged them to come and rescue him and the clerk. But no sooner did they touch the clerk than they stuck on too, and so there were seven of them running after Dullhead and his goose.

DISCUSS AS YOU READ:
WHAT WOULD YOU DO IF YOU CAME ACROSS A STRANGE PROCESSION OF PEOPLE RUNNING IN A FIELD WHILE STUCK TO EACH OTHER?

After a time they all came to a town where a King reigned whose daughter was so serious and solemn that no one could ever manage to make her laugh. So the King had decreed that whoever should succeed in making her laugh should marry her.

When Dullhead heard this he marched before the Princess with his goose and its appendages, and as soon as she saw these seven people continually running after each other she burst out laughing, and could not stop herself. Then Dullhead claimed her as his bride, but the King, who did not much fancy him as a son-in-law, made all sorts of objections, and told him he must first find a man who could drink up a whole cellarful of wine.

Dullhead bethought him of the little grey man, who could, he felt sure, help him; so he went off to the forest, and on the very spot where he had cut down the tree he saw a man sitting with a most dismal expression of face.

Dullhead asked him what he was taking so much to heart, and the man answered, "I don't know how I am ever to quench this terrible thirst I am suffering from. Cold water doesn't suit me at all. To be sure I've emptied a whole barrel of wine, but what is one drop on a hot stone?"

"I think I can help you," said Dullhead. "Come with me, and you shall drink to your heart's content." So he took him to the King's cellar, and the man sat down before the huge casks and drank and drank till he drank up the whole contents of the cellar before the day closed.

Then Dullhead asked once more for his bride, but the King felt vexed at the idea of a stupid fellow whom people called "Dullhead" carrying off his daughter, and he began to make fresh conditions. He required Dullhead to find a man who could eat a mountain of bread.

Dullhead did not wait to consider long but went straight off to the forest, and there on the same spot sat a man who was drawing in a strap as tight as he could round his body, and making a most woeful face the while. Said he, "I've eaten up a whole oven full of loaves, but what's the good of that to anyone who is as hungry as I am? I declare my stomach feels quite empty, and I must draw my belt tight if I'm not to die of starvation."

Dullhead was delighted, and said, "Get up and come with me, and you shall have plenty to eat." And he brought him to the King's Court.

Now the King had given orders to have all the flour in his kingdom brought together, and to have a huge mountain baked of it. But the man from the wood just took up his stand before the mountain and began to eat, and in one day it had all vanished.

For the third time Dullhead asked for his bride, but again the King tried to make some evasion, and demanded a ship "which could sail on land or water! When you come sailing in such a ship," said he, "you shall have my daughter without further delay."

DISCUSS AS YOU READ:
WOULD YOU HAVE GONE TO THE SAME GREAT LENGTHS AS DULLHEAD TO MARRY THE PRINCESS, IF YOU WERE HIM?

Again Dullhead started off to the forest, and there he found the little old grey man with whom he had shared his cake, and who said, "I have eaten and I have drunk for you, and now I will give you the ship. I have done all this for you because you were kind and merciful to me."

Then he gave Dullhead a ship which could sail on land or water, and when the King saw it he felt he could no longer refuse him his daughter.

So they celebrated the wedding with great rejoicings; and after the King's death Dullhead succeeded to the kingdom, and lived happily with his wife for many years after.

THE DISCUSSION

First, briefly narrate the story back.

Questions to ask after reading the story:
• How does the ending make you feel? Why does the ending make you feel that way?
• Why does the storyteller say that the first brother was "clever" and that the second brother answered the gray man "most sensibly" when they refused to give him any of their food and drink?
• Compare the three brothers and the three sisters from the inn. How are they similar? How are they different?
• What would you have done when you found the golden goose if you were Dullhead?
• Why do you think the story calls the little old man "gray"?
• Do you consider the king in the story to be dishonest?
• Why do so many people think Dullhead is stupid?
• Do the characters remind you of characters from any other story? Explain.

Listening for Echoes
Why do you think so many fairy tales include characters like the little gray man in the woods, strangely magical creatures who help or curse people depending on how other characters interact with them?

Can you think of any other stories in which the main character is given a demeaning name but he or she proves to be smarter than everyone thinks?

Additional Resources

There are many wonderful resources that can help you dive into the world of fairy tales. Here are a select few that we especially love.

• *Tending the Heart of Virtue* by Vigen Guroian (Oxford University Press, 1998)

• "Address to Young Men on How They Might Derive Benefit from Greek Literature" by St. Basil (Forgotten Books, 2017)

• *An Experiment in Criticism* by C.S. Lewis (Cambridge University Press, 2012)

• *Reading Between the Lines* by Gene Edward Veith (Crossway Books, 2013)

• *The Christian Imagination* by Leland Ryken, ed. (Shaw Books, 2002)

• *Ten Ways to Destroy the Imagination of Your Child* by Anthony Esolen (ISI Books, 2010)

• *How to Read a Book* by Mortimer Adler (Touchstone, 1972)

• *Hans Christian Andersen's Complete Fairy Tales* by Hans Christian Andersen (Multiple editions available)

• *The Complete Grimm's Fairy Tales* by Jacob Grimm and Wilhelm Grimm (Multiple editions available)

• Andrew Lang's Fairy Books. There are twelve books in this set and, while they do not have to be read in order, here is the "official" order: *Blue, Red, Green, Yellow, Pink, Grey, Violet, Crimson, Brown, Orange, Olive, Lilac* (Multiple editions available)

About the Publisher

The CiRCE Institute is a non-profit 501(c)3 organization that exists to promote and support classical education in the school and in the home. We seek to identify the ancient principles of learning, to communicate them enthusiastically, and to apply them vigorously in today's educational settings through curricula development, teacher and parent training, events, and multimedia resources.

Learn more at www.circeinstitute.com or on Facebook @circeinstitute.